Between the Doors of Life and Death

By: Dr. Hooria Noor

Between the Doors of Life and Death

Published by:
HAVAH Publishing
Ashland, Ohio

Address all inquiries to:
Dr. Hooria Noor
havahpublishing@gmail.com

ISBN: 978-1-7328114-0-9

Editor and Interior Book Layout: Amy Rice

Cover Designer: Media Vision
        (www.mediavisionpk.com)

Every attempt has been made to source properly all quotes.

Printed in the United States of America

First Edition

Contents

Healthcare is only as effective as the relationship
between the doctor and the patient.

Chapter One

High Heel Shoes

Medicine can be glamorous.

Answers to questions that were never asked start to swirl around my mind. What makes me different? What makes mine a voice to be heard? There are unique things about every human being on earth, and every story is worth being shared—but, what stories do I want to tell?

The questionnaire I had been sent started an avalanche in my mind. Most days, my duties as a doctor kept my brain far too busy to ponder anything other than my patients. This request for an interview, albeit a written interview, had disrupted my norm, and now my mind was scripting the nuances of the medical field that outsiders would never see.

No, I never wanted to be a doctor as a child. I didn't even consider the health profession until a nurse came to see my mother, and she had these heels on that went click, click, click through our home. It was the sound of authority marched out with grace. The nurse had a dignified, accomplished way about her that made me hope to be like her when I grew up.

It was probably more the heels, though, that made me want to be like her. Little 4-year-old me lived in the home of a missionary and high heels were off limits, out of the question. A smile plays around my lips as I think of how silly it might sound in an interview to admit I chose the medical field because of high-heeled shoes. Looking back, I respected this woman, saw her dignity and compassion. She was warm and kind, very professional. All these things, that a child cannot verbalize at the moment, drew me to think this was where I needed to be.

Her official title was 'Health Visitor.' She had come to visit my younger sister, to see how the baby and my mother were doing after she had been born. Her house-call really impressed my little mind. I would walk around saying that I was going to be a Health Visitor. My older sister would say, "Fine, you can be my nurse. I'm going to be a doctor." I didn't want to be her nurse though, I wanted to show up at homes, in high-heel shoes, and take care of people.

When we started elementary school, we decided that wearing high heels was the biggest fantasy of our lives. We didn't have any, so we would tie a stone to the back of our flip-flops and walk around on the concrete to hear that beloved sound of elegance and, we imagined, sophistication. That isn't why I am a doctor, but I am wearing heels.

Looking back on everything I have gone through to arrive at my own practice, in the United States: from going to medical school in Pakistan and practicing there, to retaking the exams and doing residencies here; I realized that there are other doctors, and patients alike, who need to hear it is worth it. All the studying and hard work, all the sad stories along with the amazing stories, all of it is worth the sacrifices. Missing time with family to save and change lives, missing meals and milestones— it is part of the duty of the doctor.

There may be doctors that do this for money and prestige—and that is sad for them. Most of us are in the healthcare profession because we want to make a difference. Our inner drive is compassion. Our duty is to help humans, and as a doctor, high-heels or flats, I am committed to making a difference in every life I cross paths with.

Chapter Two

Medicine and Faith

Intention counts.
"Deeds are judged by motives."
~Muhammad~

The building was made of beautiful beige stones with great landscaping; cascading flowers in brilliant yellows, purples, and pinks exploded next to every tree, sidewalk, entrance, and exit.

As I walked up the sidewalk, I saw the faces looking out from the windows, forlorn. Their eyes distant, traveling back to the internment camps they had suffered in long ago, but not long enough ago. There is no reason for human beings to suffer the way that these women had. Looking at their wrinkled faces, the creases marking time the way the hands of a clock do, I wondered if these walls held the same horror for them, trapped away from their families.

This was to be my first official job out of medical school. My spotless white lab coat, the badge hanging with my title and picture, none of it could have prepared me for the real-life lessons that were hidden behind the doors. Becoming a doctor prepares you to see illness and strive for health, but it doesn't prepare you for the brokenness that seems so far away from your own life.

This building made especially for the elderly, existing highlighted the differences in cultures, a world apart. In Pakistan, sons and daughters take care of their

9

elderly family members, but we are not aware of the level of care that is being provided in the home.

The concept of a retirement or nursing home didn't exist. Likewise, parents took care of their children until they were married, and even then, some extended family arrangements existed. There weren't thoughts of throwing a child out into the world at 18-years-old and expecting them to survive. Children would stay at home until they were married, and the children always figured out how the elderly parents would be cared for. Even after marriage, sons stay at home unless they had to move for their job. In Islamic culture, the sons take care of the parents.

In my culture, parents are a blessing, and we take care of our elderly parents. It is a responsibility that is not taken lightly. It is seen as disrespectful to not take care of elderly parents, it is a blessing to be able to do so. The Quran says to spread our wings of humility on parents, and to pray mercy on them, like they did for us when we were young. This concept of retirement communities and nursing homes is different for me. I am not trying to judge the practice; surely, it creates jobs. It is hard for caregivers with hearts to watch the patients, that could easily be cared for at home, be abandoned by children who never come to visit.

The elderly parent will ask, "Where is my son, my daughter? Where are the children?" And, there isn't an appropriate answer: 'These children you raised, through sacrifice and love, they don't come.' There were also times the children came, but due to dementia, the parent wouldn't remember, so the staff would kindly remind the patient.

So, the nurses and caregivers say things like, "Oh, it's almost dinner. Are you hungry?" These diversion methods don't work well, and the patient will continue to ask for family. Caregivers will answer that they don't know, and sometimes we reach out to family, to try to bring them together with their aging parents. Too often, there is nothing that can be done—due to distance or time constraints, and we do the best we can to keep the elderly patient company.

There are the extreme cases where the patient is clearly better suited to be in skilled care facilities, where their complex needs are better met, that improve their quality of life. But it remains that there are many patients in nursing homes that could be with their families. The luxury of having someplace to put the elderly shouldn't take the place of personal responsibility. Where there is no sacrifice, is there really love?

Being a doctor is my duty in life. My care for my patients goes much deeper than just someone to oversee them. I came here, to a Jewish nursing home, because I know what religious persecution looks and feels like. We were under threat of death because of our faith. That's why we came here, leaving our homes and careers in Pakistan. These women had experienced atrocities in World War II. It seemed sad that they were stuck behind the walls of our building, trapped again against their will, away from loved ones. That gloomy reality never escaped my mind as I saw their sweet faces and held their hands. Some of the elderly haven't been touched by another human being since their spouses have passed or since they have been placed in the home. Slight touch can help with their depression. Therefore, I made an effort to touch their hands or shoulder when I interacted with them.

This nursing home was looking for a doctor, and I saw an opportunity to give love and care to people who needed it most. Perhaps, I thought, breaking cultural barriers will assist in the healing of minds and hearts, seeing their faces has already stirred compassion and love in me. Prayer has been a huge part of my medical career to date, and with faith being the center of my life, it will continue.

My prejudice towards the way nursing homes were used to house the elderly was changed by Clare. Again, I wasn't open to children not caring for elderly parents, because in Pakistan, this wasn't an option. Clare came to us at 98-years-old, and her daughter had been caring for her for 15 years.

Her eldest daughter expressed that they couldn't care for her anymore. The bedsores on her hips were incredibly painful and deep, proof the daughters had reached their capacity of care for their beloved mother. Clare's children dearly loved her, but they were having to work to survive. This is the struggle for survival—the bills don't stop coming and retirement doesn't grow, if you aren't working. Sometimes, I wonder if the system would change, in America, that maybe these things wouldn't happen. I found myself trying to make sense of the culture.

Her daughter had so much guilt about putting Clare in the nursing home, but we were able to bring relief to her bedsores and prevent further damage to her sore body. Our trained staff knows to turn patients and prop them in different directions, so their body isn't putting all the weight in one place. Clare's daughter visited and remained a large part of Claire's care, but seeing her love for her mother softened my misgivings about this practice. Even though I had concerns, and if I am being honest—I thought children should care for their parents like my culture does, I was more confident in that moment that I could make a difference.

My next patient was a 108-year-old woman named Ana. She was always dignified and well put together. She had her shirt tucked into her pants, her hair just so; the nurse told me she was particular. Her mind was still strong; there was no sign of dementia or Alzheimer's. She would make it a point to walk down to my office every month, all by herself. She didn't use a walker. Ana was very independent.

After a few months of seeing her, I got used to her routine, "Doctor Noor, how am I doing?" Ana would wait until I was done listening to her heart and checking her over to ask. She would tuck her shirt back into her pants before asking, her voice strong and unquavering.

"Ana, your heart and kidneys are strong! I am amazed at your health, you are doing great! Any secrets to living this long?" I was happy for her; what a privilege to work with someone who has seen over a century of life!

Ana started crying, inconsolable, "I am so tired! I don't want to live anymore." Her sobs stirred something in me; this moment would never be erased from my brain. After all, she has survived the Holocaust, decades of memories of lost loved ones, building a life after a world tragedy. She was weary and no longer wanted to live, yet her body failed to let her leave. She had outlived her parents, as a child should, some of her children, and the love of her life.

"Ana, I am sorry that you took that news as bad. When your time comes, I will make sure that you are comfortable, but until then, we are going to keep you healthy!" I meant it too. I loved my patients and prayed for them.

Ana feared dying. When I would try to find out her wishes, she would begin to sob at the thought of death. Her wish and fear were the same. This thing she wanted—death—alluded her, yet it frightened her as well.

Death is a scary concept—the great unknown. We live and breathe expecting good things to happen or accepting the bad things that happen. We are so used to existing that the prospect of not existing becomes an abyss that we dare not spend too long exploring in the depths of our minds. Somehow, even though Ana was disinterested in living any longer, she was equally terrified of death. Maybe, she hoped that she would go in her sleep, unaware that she was passing. Many patients who claim they are 'ready to die,' yet when it was their time, they were horrified, so scared, that they would beg us to save them. We would comfort them and take care of their pain to try to keep them from existing on machines and intubated.

Ana turned away from me, signaling that our conversation was over. Looking at the back of her, I saw strength and weary courage. Empathy flooded my heart as I realized that at 108-years-old, the world wasn't even the same place that she had once known and felt comfortable being a part of.

Emigrating to the United States, from Pakistan, had changed my world. There had been religious persecution in Pakistan, for my family and me, with threats of death, but I knew she had seen things she had never again been able to speak about.

I turned and listened to the calming click of my heels as I stood to open the door. Ana walked, on her own volition, back towards her room. The nurse tagged along to steady her should she falter, but Ana never stumbled.

When I closed the door to my office, I sat at my desk and let the feelings overwhelm me. There haven't been many times that I delivered great news and had it taken as negative. As I let that sink in, I began to shift papers around on my desk and saw a letter that stopped me in my tracks. In the left-hand corner was the Star of David and a return address to a Jewish medical journal. Curiosity rose and there I saw a questionnaire concerning my care of Jewish retirees.

Reading over the questions, an angle appeared:

1.   How do you feel being a Muslim doctor in a Jewish nursing home?

Thoughts about not filling out the interview crossed my mind, yet it was an opportunity to break down some barriers to religious differences that I wanted to meet head-on. I began to pray that God would guide my answers, so that they had the most effect in the hearts of the readers. Peace came over me, so, I wrote:

There is no religion in medicine. The doctor is the doctor, and the patient is the patient. There is no gender in medicine—the doctor is the doctor, and the patient is the patient.

The relationship between doctor and patient is built on the basis of mutual trust and respect. The relationship is beneficent and non-maleficence, meaning that I am there to help and to provide care and to do no harm.

It is sad that there is an understanding that has developed between the Muslim and the Jew that sets us at odds with one another, when we are cousins. We are all the progeny of Prophet Abraham.

Ultimately, I see my duty as a doctor to be providing care. If my attention and care through one hug or smile, through kind words or encouragement, provides a higher standard of living for my patients, then I have been a successful doctor. The patients' comfort and acceptance of my role in their lives far exceeds societal prejudices.

To date, the people in my care have expressed that they are happy with the level of healthcare that I provide, and I appreciate you providing a platform for me to share that medicine reaches across every cultural and religious line that anyone would like to draw in the sand. It is an honor that you have chosen me to interview out of all the other Muslim and Jewish doctors that work with patients of the opposite faith.

2.   If you could sum up, in one word, your care style, what would that word be? Please explain.

Compassionate.

Compassion is the most important aspect in medicine. My goal is to put myself in my patient's shoes and try to see where they are coming from. It is often called the 'Golden Rule,' but it is best explained as caring for my patients the way that I would want myself or someone in my family cared for.

Compassionate care seeks to find out what the patient wants and why, so that we can make decisions that provide integrity to the people we are treating. A doctor without compassion is not a doctor at all, much like food without any spice is devoid of flavor.

If there is anything else, I can answer for you to help you with this article, please do not hesitate to reach out to me. I would be happy to continue the conversation.

My door stayed shut while I thought through the best answers for the questionnaire. The solitude was appreciated as I prayed over my answers

Like my Holocaust survivor patients at the nursing home, I have seen things that I wish I had never seen, by the writing of this book. Some people may think I chose to see these things, due to the nature of being a doctor, but nothing readies a human being to see the worst-case scenarios. Not even med school.

In nursing homes, when someone enters the facility, it is more than likely their last abode, their final resting place. I remember the first time I went to see a dementia patient in her room, I was alone with her. She was talking to herself and did not communicate with me, it was like I wasn't even there. It was hard to see that, and I felt a little uncomfortable. As time went on, I saw these patients as my best friends, and I loved taking care of them. This was not something I was used to seeing from practicing in Southeast Asia.

In Pakistan, my dear husband found out from our town that they needed a doctor to work with the women of our hometown. Most of the people in our hometown belonged to our sect. The hospital would resemble what the West calls a 'mission hospital,' because many towns were serviced from this hospital. People would come to be seen for prorated fees or free, whatever they could or couldn't afford was given to them, regardless of their ability to pay.

He convinced me that this was an honor and a way to serve our community that had lasting results. His reminders that this may be my last chance to serve our community before we emigrated to America was what sealed the deal for me. Obstetrics and gynecological issues, here I come. We had just had our second daughter, Sarah, at the time. This was a huge sacrifice to make, with a new baby, but it was necessary and important.

The hospital in the town I was raised in services about 100 miles of area. People from surrounding areas would bring their relatives to this hospital, because we took care of the poor people for free. There were four months out of the year when there was no obstetrician or gynecologists in the town to help the female patients.

There were times when there was no anesthesiologist available.

This small community hospital was blessed by the prayers of the elders: Even with minimal resources, results were always blessed with success. That was the biggest difference that I can say made a huge impact on me: Seeing the power of prayer at work at this hospital confirmed what I knew from my own life, but it also solidified that prayer needs to be in the hospitals and other care facilities around the world.

During riot times, our sect was socially boycotted by the rest of society. They would stop supplying our milk and other goods from surrounding farms. Things always seemed to be taken care of for the hospital, despite the social boycotts. They never seemed to be able to completely leave us alone: Whenever someone was sick, their families would bring them to our community hospital. It was not a secret that there were many miracles and people cured due to blessings.

My husband had given me the car. This was the car we had just purchased, and that was a big deal! Buying a car was not easy, as there was no financing available. As a married couple with two kids, we had to save thousands of rupees to buy a car with cash. I had the girls with me, so he said that I needed to keep the car. Qamar, my husband, had decided he was going to come back and forth by coach bus.

I had never taken formal driving lessons. No one checked the licenses of drivers, only rarely when cops stopped drivers, but more normally they would ask for some money to pay them, and they would let you go free on the bribe. Qamar just gave me one lesson and expected that I would drive fine, but it was a stick shift, so you can imagine, I ended up scratching the side of the car the first time I drove while trying to park in the porch of the hospital.

The second time, I decided to take my daughters to Friday prayers. It was extremely congested; I lost control and ended up bumping into a car, but strangely enough the guy in the blue Suzuki just looked at me. He did not come out or yell at me!

Relief flooded me as I thanked God that even though I had bumped this guy hard, he had controlled any emotions that might have risen, and my girls didn't have to see anger from another driver. My heart was racing though, because drivers do not want their cars banged up, no matter where they live.

The next morning, I found out that he was the administrator of the hospital! He nicely advised me to drive carefully, after I had my already scheduled meeting with him. After that, I decided not to take the car for Friday prayers. This still makes me cringe and chuckle, at the same time.

It is these moments that remind you how small the world can be. What are the odds that, out of all the vehicles and people in the parking lot, I bumped the hospital administrator? Being reminded to drive carefully by your boss is humiliating, even if they are kind about it.

I remember a patient came to see me in my first few days of practice, who did not have any children after 15 years of marriage. I examined her and advised her to come back for more testing. She came back after a month or so with the news that she was expecting. The whole family brought in flowers and sweets for the doctors. In Pakistan, expressions of gratitude were the norm.

We used to perform a test called post coital test for infertility; on or around the patient's ovulation days. The female patient was advised to come to the office after having sexual intercourse. I would examine and take a sample of the vaginal secretions, then run to the lab, a few blocks away, to look at the specimen under the microscope. This helped us to comment on the sperm count, mobility, and the elasticity of the vaginal secretion for evidence of ovulation. Many times, ladies would conceive after performing this test. This would mean more sweets and fresh flowers.

One good tradition at this hospital in my hometown was that all procedures done at this facility were preceded by silent prayers. We were very aware of the power of prayer. Doctors, nurses, and other staff members would raise their hands for prayer for the patients often, and we saw many miracles accompany the patients there.

I remember treating my husband's first cousin, who was in her late thirties and did not have any children, even after trying for 18 years. She was given infertility drugs because it looked like she would not be able to conceive a child naturally. One evening, she came for a follow-up visit and it was determined that she was expecting. There was a tiny fetal heart beating!

Everyone was celebrating and excited. But after three to four weeks, she started spotting. The ultrasound revealed no fetal heartbeat was present. We had to perform D and C, since her body wasn't naturally expelling all the tissue from the miscarriage. All the nurses were crying. The procedure started with heartfelt prayers for this lady and for her to have a healthy baby in the future.

After a few weeks, she conceived again! This time, she had a full-term pregnancy and a very healthy baby boy, after 18 years of marriage. This precious baby boy was followed by another boy and then a girl. Resources were meek at our hospital, but blessings were enormous. Many times, we would use homeopathic solutions, like pulsatilla to help with urinary tract issues and other women's issues. In Pakistan, we used pulsatilla for breech babies. We would give it to them, and in a week the baby would be positioned normally. This is a great example of why I carry prayer into my practice here in the United States. God didn't stop hearing my prayers because I crossed the ocean. He didn't stop caring for people because the continent is different.

One evening, I was alone on duty. During those days, we did not have an anesthesiologist. Anybody who would come for delivery, if there was any delay in the progression of labor, we had to transfer them to a hospital one hour away. That meant we had to make decisions in time for them to be transported and see what was happening early to give our patients the chance to make it to the closest hospital with emergency services. It was very stressful!

Bad situations don't wait until the situation is ideal and the right people are in place to save a life are scrubbed up. Unfortunately, life threatening situations can happen so fast there isn't time to respond, and we would pray before every shift that God would protect every patient we saw and give us wisdom and discernment to make decisions rapidly. The human condition makes it so we sometimes think the best when the very worst is happening. Therefore, treating family can be so challenging—our discernment and decision-making skills are marred by our relationship with the patient.

My aunt came to the hospital in labor on a day I'll never forget. She informed me that she usually progresses rapidly, so I should be ready. This was her third baby, and she was anticipating that she would deliver within a few hours of her arrival at the hospital. I advised her to come be admitted to the labor ward, but the labor was not moving forward as expected once she was there.
Hour after hour kept going by; it was taking a long time for the head to come down, as the baby's head was not flexed. She was looking towards the sky; this kind of positioning of the head takes a very long time to descend. Sometimes we had to change the head position in the uterus, and sometimes these labors end up in caesarian section. But there was no anesthesiologist!

My aunt kept on asking, "Why is it taking so long?" She was nine centimeters dilated already. There was no time for transferring her to the hospital but keeping her without progress was very risky. For times like this I had fixed a corner in the labor ward where I would go to scrub, but in this corner, I would talk to God, directly praying from the depths of my heart. So, it seemed like I was getting scrubbed for the baby, but inside I was praying hard for my aunt to be safe through this and for the baby to survive. As soon as I finished praying, I was called by the nurse, the baby was coming! I thanked God as I started to run over to deliver my cousin. His mighty hand had worked quickly, ensuring that both my aunt and the baby would be fine.

This corner was my favorite place to go in harrowing times. I would take the time to pray. There was no phone in the labor ward. If you needed help or to call a consultant, you had to take your scrubs off and walk a block away to make a phone call. Due to low staff at our hospital, this was unfortunate. In bad emergency situations, decisions had to be made about who could be spared from the room to go for that walk. I had taken that walk when I was very concerned about a patient, and even though the maximum walk time was probably only five minutes, or less, but it felt like hours. I was able to get ahold of the blood bank, a surgeon, and a colleague doctor.

One night, I was on call, a lady who was full-term in her pregnancy came in with concerns. I did an ultrasound and discovered that she was carrying a dead baby; there was no fetal heartbeat. She was in labor to deliver the corpse, and I was the bearer of bad news.

I started her on a drip; this was her second baby. She had come from a village. After a few hours of labor, the nurse called me to deliver the baby, as she was fully dilated, but just after the baby was delivered, she started bleeding profusely. There was no time to get help! She only had one peripheral line that was running normal saline, and she kept on bleeding. I tried to get extra lines and center lines but was not successful. She kept on bleeding and bleeding until I was very concerned.

For me to call for blood bank people meant I had

to leave her and walk the full block to call the doctor who oversaw blood bank, as there was only one nurse with me in the labor ward. This meant that there would only one of us trying to save this woman who had just delivered a stillborn baby.

My patient was in DIC, which is a condition where all the clotting factors in the blood get consumed by widespread clotting, therefore the bleeding was profuse. It couldn't be stopped, and this patient expired right in front of me. I felt so helpless that I could not help this life. I decided right then I didn't want to be a doctor anymore.

For three days, I did not go to work. I kept crying. Then the director called me to explain that saving this patient would have been difficult, even in a very advanced setting, and many of the factors were beyond my capacity to handle. That didn't make losing her easier, it just simply meant that she could have died no matter how good the machines and amenities were.

We all have a time to die, but for doctors and people in the medical field—we are doing everything we can to save our patients. It is very hard to face mortality. Period. It doesn't matter whether the patient is young or old, ill or well, weak or strong. We are all pulling for our patients. I have also noticed that because I pray as hard as I do, I tend to have a hard time with my patients passing. I expect God to hear and answer my prayers. He is faithful. That day is the day I realized that His sovereignty some-times says no, and He sometimes let's life pass. That doesn't make Him less God, it just makes us more human and dependent on His answers to our prayers.

I resumed my responsibilities at the hospital, but even now I cannot forgive myself for that night not being able to save that woman. Her life leaving her eyes has stuck with me until I pray harder and fight harder for my patients to survive. I dare not say I take it more seriously than other doctors, but perhaps that would be a true assessment of my heart. I would also like to say that I never lost a patient again, and that everyone lived happily ever after, but that would be a lie.

When I left Pakistan and had to start all over in the United States, I chose another door. Bringing life into the world is precious and necessary, but I knew I was ready to handle helping people pass through the door to eternity.

I have my father to thank for this decision, but we will talk about that in the next chapter.

Chapter Three

Saddest Case:
The Importance of Listening
to Patients

Listening is easier when the heart is involved.

When I am asked questions about being a doctor, I often get questions about the cases that have affected me the most. Every person that I encounter changes my life. No one seems to accept that answer. Let me start with this: The things that affect you the most are the people that are closest to you. Then, the ripple effect begins.

As a doctor, I see more death than most people would care to see. I have also seen more life. There is the dichotomy of life and death, male and female, light and dark, those parallels continue, forever. I am blessed to be a chapter in many people's stories.

There is one chapter of my own story that changed the course of my life. When I first made it to the United States, my family was in the process of building careers and lives all over again. As if that wasn't enough, my father was diagnosed with cancer.

At the time, we called it the "c" word, because we couldn't bear to say the word aloud. My dad was still young and in his right mind, as sharp as ever. To see his decline was more than our hearts could bear.

My final pregnancy, with my son, was an exciting time. I was in a new land, the United States of America, joining my family again from Pakistan. The pregnancy had come full-term and I was set to deliver in two weeks. My father told my sister, who is also a doctor, that when he eats, food gets stuck in his chest. Of course, she told him that he needed to see a doctor to be checked out, and she volunteered to take him.

The doctor ordered a test and within 24 hours, he had a diagnosis. Esophageal cancer. This was a catastrophe for our whole family. The initial bomb blast of the diagnosis resonated fear and anger for a long time to come.

Then my sister and I jumped into action. We started running through his treatment options, telling him what might help prolong his life. Losing a parent was something none of us were ready for, and I am sure there is never a way to be prepared for that loss. Our father told us that he was deciding against chemotherapy and other treatments. He matter-of-factly informed us that he would allow nature to take its course.

So, the cancer diagnosis was October 13, and my son was born on October 24. My abba jaan got everyone together for a family portrait. It was a beautiful memory, and my son is in the picture, so that was a blessing. With him being my last child, we get to enjoy that portrait as complete, with all the grandkids.

Watching our father struggle with cancer was more than we could endure, so all five sisters got together and sat around abba jaan. We pleaded with him to give himself a chance, explained that treatment might change the prognosis for him. We needed him, and the grandkids needed him. He was a pillar to our family; we were not going to allow him to brush this conversation away. Finally, he agreed to do treatment, "Okay, if you all insist, I'll go."

A new chapter began, right at that moment. We began taking him for opinions. We found out he wasn't a surgery candidate. His only option was a laser treatment to remove the tumor. At that time, they added a feeding tube to aid in his ability to get the sustenance that he needed.

The next step was chemotherapy. We had to watch as he became sicker and sicker. Abba jaan was reluctant to take pain medications, which left him in constant agony. We had grown up learning that pain medications are not good, that they may help with the pain, but that they cause other issues.

Most of his remaining life, from diagnosis until death, October to May, was spent in and out of hospitals. Though, if I must admit, it was more in than out. Ami, my mother, would go to work and then go to spend time with him in the hospital, running herself ragged to provide and be by his side. At times, she made time to come see the baby, because she knew that my heart was broken by my inability to drive to see my father like I wanted to.

My sisters took great care of abba jaan. They provided the nursing and comfort care that he needed, so that he would not have to have outside help. At times, someone would come stay with my children and the baby so I could go see him, but I could never stay long enough to satisfy the daughter's heart in me. I was close to abba jaan, and this was not the way things were supposed to be.

I made my sister promise that if he started to pass, she would get ahold of me immediately, so I could get there to be by his side. Arrangements were made, in that case, for a friend to come get me, then stay in the car with the two little girls and baby, because I didn't drive at that time. My sister was there with him, but she never called. Her heart was in the right place. She had figured it would be more painful for me if I knew but couldn't get there, so she didn't pick up the phone. She knew of the driving issue and that my husband was at work. She didn't know that plans were already in place.

After I found out, I went down to the morgue and sat with him for a little while. When people die, they (the hospitals or places where they die) try to get rid of the bodies so fast! Within 24 hours. It's too fast for the mourning families.

When dad died, we were not able to get his body released from the morgue, like the custom in Pakistan. There, a family would have the body in their home, and they would have had the freedom to mourn and sit in the presence of their loved one for a day or two, in case someone was traveling. If everyone who was coming had made it, the body was then buried immediately. Abba jaan wanted to be buried close to where we were, as soon as possible, not be taken back to Pakistan.

This was our first brush with death in the United States, and we had no idea what to do. We were surprised to find out that my father, Yusef, in his weakened state, suffering from cancer, had made all the plans for his funeral. All the arrangements were prepared by him and that task had helped him maintain his dignity while his body was failing him.

This was an incredibly tough time for our whole family, but I took it extremely hard because I had not been able to be there for him, like I wanted to be there. In this new land, I had two small daughters and a newborn son with no car. My immobility left my mother, Ayesha, caring for him on her own while she navigated working to provide for their needs. Feelings of guilt cropped up after his passing that I had not been able to be present more.

My last visit with abba jaan was meaningful. I had sat with him, knowing that he had pain, and my instinct was to put my hand on his chest. I just sat with him, feeling his heartbeat and monitoring his breathing, while comforting him. I remember wondering if this was the last time I would be with him, hoping desperately that it was not the final visit. We were able to talk freely and just enjoy our time together. I am forever grateful to God for this time.

His passing spurred me to regain my medical license in the United States. I committed to work with the elderly, in loving memory of my father, who was only 68-years-old when he passed away. That is too early to leave this life, but I had to wake up and realize that God knows best, and He knows His plan, even when we struggle to understand what the purpose of our suffering is.

There was one other lesson from my father's journey that I have always kept with me: It was a contrast from Pakistan to the United States that I struggled with then and have learned a lot from since his passing. When he was sick, and trying to navigate his diagnosis, he would ask the oncologists while they made their rounds, "Will I recover?"

Their answer, "No, you will not," would always take the breath out of our lungs. It seemed so harsh. That cold answer was hard on him and us. Abba jaan's face became pale and his eyes filled with disappointment. I would sit and think that the people treating abba jaan were so unkind, that they didn't care that they were causing harm to us mentally and emotionally; never mind that abba jaan was physically getting worse before our eyes.

In Pakistan, they won't even tell you that you have a serious illness. It is believed that the patient dies faster when they know, so they would hide detrimental diagnoses. Here, the doctors are brutally honest. They were very open and truthful, operating in the belief that patients have the right to know what is going on with their bodies and disease.

There is absolutely an ethical duty, for every doctor, to be truthful. There is a difference in hearing the truth or not being told, and the delivery of bad news to a patient.

When I must deliver bad news, I think back to what abba jaan and our family went through with his cancer. I have honed the art of delivery in these moments to be empathetic and caring for the patients (who deserve the best care all the time); they deserve dignity in the moments that will reign as the scariest times of their lives.

The Dr. Noor's 'How to Talk to Patients' rules are:
1. Sit face-to-face.
2. Hold the patient's hands. Show empathy.
3. Tell the truth with faith— "No one can tell when someone will die. It's in the hands of God. What we can do is make life comfortable for you." I also tell patients, "I can treat your symptoms, and I won't abandon you or leave you alone." Once a patient is referred to hospice, some doctors leave their patients. I try to stay with my patients and not abandon them in their time of need.
4. I would stress the prognosis, by the book— through the lens of medical understanding. I would also suggest to the patient to enjoy the best things today and leave tomorrow in the hands of God, to try to accomplish everything that was important, and take the time to connect with family and make things right with people if that was necessary.

If I seem to have oversimplified the process, it is not on purpose. I build rapport with my patients, and I have come to know many of them over many years, so I tailor my conversation to their personality. There are different schools of thought when it comes to bringing faith and God into medicine. Some say we should not, some say we should, but I have elected to keep my faith as part of my practice. Patients are always welcome to seek a different doctor to care for them, so it is not harming anyone to abide by faith in the medical field. I have seen it do a lot of good.

It seems that when you've been in healthcare for as long as I have, the patients' stories start to flow. As I sit here, I think about all the patients that needed someone to listen. A PhD doctor came to me one time. His daughter was an eye doctor, and she sent him over. He was exasperated, "My doctor is ignoring me!" That was the beginning of our visit, he continued, "Something's not right!"

"We will order some bloodwork and look at your records from before." I reassured him that we would do a full workup, to calm his mind. Abnormalities showed in the results from previous tests, so I ordered more bloodwork. The medical records showed slightly abnormal liver function. This new bloodwork was incredibly abnormal, so we went right to a CT scan. There was a tumor in his liver! We began treatment immediately. He had been looking for help, and no one would listen to him because he was still young, in his sixties, and relatively healthy.

His last day was spent telling jokes with me. It amazed me how funny he was. He would tell a joke, then I would. He also shared poetry. We were able to laugh and laugh. It was evident that he was in his last moments. I had offered to stay with him while his daughter went home to be with her children for a few hours. I went about my day, and then when the day was winding down, I found out that he had passed. This news was bittersweet, but I was able to find solace in the knowledge that he had been laughing earlier in the day. I was happy to have shared the laughs with him; I'm glad I took the time.

During my career, there have been patients who seemed to be alone in this world that I have cared for. That is a sad way to be in this world, as it can be lonely when there are many people that love you. Greg was a homeless person that we saw at the nursing home. He had been living in his tent, in the middle of winter when the temperatures drop below freezing, and he had tried to burn a gas stove to get warm.

When his tent caught on fire, Greg was taken to the hospital where he was fed and looked over. Hospitals have social workers that are assigned, during admissions, to assess the best possible disposition for patients and families who might need guidance or help. It takes a doctor to make a decision of this magnitude about the capability to make decisions. If a patient is mentally capable to make decisions, they can choose to go live in a jungle, and we can't stop them. If a patient is deemed incapable, we can make well-being decisions on their behalf. They had decided due to the hypothermia and his confused disoriented mental status that he was not capable of living alone on the streets in this condition. Because of his mental confusion he was deemed incapable of making decisions. Once the doctors that took Greg's case deemed him incapable of living independently, he was admitted to our nursing home.

In my naivety, I thought Greg would love the nursing home. He would no longer have to scrounge around in the garbage for food. No longer would he need to dumpster dive for his wants and needs. We were feeding him three square large warm meals each day, and he was welcome to get snacks when he wanted. He had a warm bed with heated blankets and the shower available. He could watch television, play board games with other residents, get involved in the various activities that we offered so he could make friends. I figured that Greg was happier than he had been in a long time, but I was wrong.

Greg missed his freedom. He would often request our social workers to evaluate him for his capability to live independently again. Greg kept our nurses on their toes, so on the day that he complained about chest pain, the nurse thought he was just spoofing to get out of the nursing home. He would tease them sometimes that he would escape on a hospital visit, and this nurse did not want to be chewed out by a hospital social worker who also knew that our dear Greg was a flight risk.

The nurses would see their patients and compile a list of who I needed to give extra attention to the examination, since I cannot be with every patient all the time. On this particular day, Greg's name was not on the list.

This was the day that changed our lives, especially the nurse's life. Figuring that he was looking for a way to leave the building, the nurse disregarded the complaints of chest pain. In her mind, he was just making excuses, so she made the decision to ignore his complaints entirely, but she ended up mentioning to me that he was complaining of chest pain, in passing.

I immediately went to visit him, "Do you have chest pain right now?"

He looked at me and answered, "No." A person who is complaining of something to gain an outcome, like escaping the facility, would have said 'yes' in that moment. That was when I knew for a fact that he had been telling the truth, as I suspected.

I told him, "The next time you have chest pain, you tell your nurse. I will see to it that you are taken to the hospital and checked out immediately." At that time, I ordered an EKG, just to look. The results were non-specific, so I let the nurse know what I had told Greg, so we could be on the same page. This was at one in the afternoon.

Later that day, between three and four in the afternoon, Greg complained of chest pain again and informed his nurse that he needed surgery. He was sent to the emergency room where his symptoms were ignored again, as he was "seeking attention," based on their assessment.

Not too much later, he was sent back to the nursing home. He passed away that night while he was sleeping. The next day, the ER called to say that his chest x-ray was abnormal, and he might have an aneurysm. We informed them that, sadly, he was no longer living.

My rule is to always believe patients, ALL OF THE TIME. There are medical professionals who make snap judgments of patients: "Oh, they're a drug addict, that's why they want more pain meds." That is wrong. A doctor can assess a patient and see that maybe they do need more help in the pain department. The importance of listening to a patient's complaints can be the difference of life and death.

Who better knows their body than the person with the body? It is imperative that medical professionals stop labeling patients before hearing them. Rule number one is to listen, truly listen.

The doctor-patient relationship is developed on trust. If you don't believe your patient, you can't treat them. Whenever I have students shadow me, I remind them time and again to always listen to and always believe their patients.

There was no one to contact to tell them that Greg had passed away. His unkempt appearances and decisions to live on his own, away from society, had given him the status of a social pariah.

This is not an expose' of the medical establishment to which I belong. This is a simple plea to mankind, in our quest to elevate knowledge and understanding, that we remember why such elevation is important…for other human beings. If I had to rate our level of care for Greg, I would have given us a solid ten, on a scale from 1 to 10, until his final day. Our staff became too accustomed to his escape speeches to recognize when he really needed our help and that has haunted all of us.

From time to time, we all see people in need. Do we assess them through the eyes of judgment? Or do we see a human being that God made and loves? How does our treatment of people change based on our assessment? This was a learning experience for the staff, I explained that we have a responsibility to see through the circumstances of those in need.

There was a story shared recently, that someone brought to my attention. It was about a retired veteran, emaciated beyond recognition. Every rib bone jutting out, a large tumor protruding from his head, and when he was on a person's property they accosted him, "What do you think you are doing on my lawn?"

Of course, this was in a rich neighborhood, and the homeless man answered, "I am looking for a place to die. Please let me be."

The man whose yard it was became angry. At himself. Here was a human being suffering when food is so cheap, and no one had seen this man for so long that he was dying, in the bushes, like an animal. How sad that our society can overlook those in need until they, out of necessity, are looking for a place to die. Greg was that patient that reminded me that every human being deserves a level of dignity that we can give when we close our human eyes and look through our hearts.

Here are some more examples of physicians needing to listen to their patients: I tell these stories to urge readers, that may be patients, to keep looking for the right doctor. If you feel something is wrong, make sure that you keep searching for someone to listen and believe you. If you are a medical professional reading this, maybe you will look within to see that you can remember your own experiences to remind you to slow down and listen, believing that the patient has come seeking help because they need it, not just the meds.

There was a 21-year-old woman, named Gina, who at the time, was the same age as my son. She was a twin, which was charming, as they were both beautiful young women. She complained of chest pain, and no one wanted to believe that a 21-year-old could be having any serious issues.

It struck me when Gina said, "My grandma thinks I'm faking."

"Did you go to the emergency room?" I asked, trying to get to the bottom of her pain.

"No, no one believes me," she sadly answered.

I began my full history and examination and

ordered tests. When she had been 15 or 16, she had a leg amputated due to bone cancer. I was determined to figure out what was going on, so I ordered a CT scan of her chest and an echocardiogram. We found a tumor in her heart. The same type of tumor that had taken her leg years prior.

Within a few months of the workup, she was dead. She had two beautiful young children who no longer had their mother. What a sad reality! Could there have been a different outcome if someone had listened sooner? We will never know.

The problem is that for many young women complaining of chest pains, they are told that there is no other explanation than atypical chest pain, radiating from muscles and not from the heart itself. It doesn't do any good to ask, 'what if?' when someone dies, but it does bode well to send patients for more testing sooner, rather than finding things too late.

These stories don't end. Gina's mother gave me an update recently, many years later, and the children are troubled since losing their mother. Their father is in trouble with the law often, and Gina's son is following in his footsteps, even though his grandmother has adopted him. She has been incredibly depressed since the twin sister was in a wreck last year that shattered her leg, and due to severe hoarding issues, she could lose her daughter's children. When someone passes, the story doesn't end, the plot changes which means our compassion must continue. We cannot be less thankful for the blessings all around us. Everyone is dealing with the challenges in their lives.

Another example of listening to patients was a woman in her sixties, named Sarah. She saw another doctor who had sought help from various doctors. They kept telling her she was depressed and to take her antidepressants. When she came to me, she was exasperated by their lackadaisical treatment of her symptoms.

I decided to run a battery of tests, and we found colon cancer. Sarah was my patient for many years, but many times when I would see her, she would mention, "Other doctors just thought I was depressed." It is important to push through simple diagnoses when you think there is something seriously wrong. You know your body better than anyone else.

When a patient comes to a doctor, it is important for us to put ourselves in their shoes. I wouldn't go wait in an office, to wait in a room, to see a doctor if there was nothing wrong with me. I would only put myself through all the waiting and worrying if I was concerned that something was wrong with me. When a patient comes to me, I look into the appropriate tests to investigate their symptoms quickly and accurately to gain answers for them. It's the ethical and right thing to do.

I was devastated to hear another person had been crying out for help, but no one would listen. I wonder, how many more people does this happen to across the nation? What about when we compound that to look at the world? I don't want to be the doctor that turns a patient's concerns away only to find out that the patient had something serious wrong with them. I prefer to err on the side of checking all possibilities. Many times, doctors want to order tests, but sometimes our hands are tied because of insurance companies requiring approval for certain tests or scans before the patient can receive the tests we have ordered.

There is so much a doctor sees and most times no one will ever hear about any of the people that have lost their lives; sometimes, only their families are aware of their lives. Doctors that care for their patients are always affected, especially in internal medicine practices where I care for people from the age of 16 to 112, or later. Not many of us can get used to the sad cases that we see.

We rejoice when we see patients thriving and doing well. In the field that I have chosen, dealing with internal medicine, there are patients that won't recover from what we find through testing. That is a difficult thing to know that some patients won't thrive again. Getting used to death and dying hasn't happened yet, even after decades of practicing medicine in Pakistan and the United States.

On the other end of the spectrum, when bringing life into the world, it isn't always as easy as a woman's water breaking, some contractions, controlled breathing, then a squalling baby with clean hair and perfect pink cheeks is welcomed into the mother and father's life to live happily ever after. How we all wish this was the case!

Television has done a huge disservice to the future generations, because while there are examples of distress on some shows, most movies and programs show a normative process for birthing mothers. Some shows may highlight new fads like water birth, or the old norms like c-sections and vaginal birth, but most make the process short and sweet the common occurrence. Ultimately, there is a myriad of things that can go wrong at such a joyous time. That is why medical training is so important, because no two cases are alike.

When I first came to America and encountered the baby shower. I thought it was odd to give a mother gifts before the baby was born, gifts that could wait until the baby was here and healthy. When a woman is in her third trimester, she is most uncomfortable, and she needs the most rest, as her body prepares for the birthing process that is coming. This is the time people throw baby showers requiring the expectant mother to be engaged in unnecessary activity, bombarding her with some heavy gifts.

Due to my experience in labor wards, the idea was daunting. In Pakistan, people came bearing gifts once the baby and mother were settled in at home. I often wondered, at first, what would happen to the families where the baby passed away and what a sad reminder all the material things would be to the grieving parents.

There is another case, from Pakistan, that still saddens me to think of it. I remember there was a lady with preeclampsia, which is where blood pressure goes way too high in women that formerly had normal blood pressure and protein spilling into the urine. They also start to see swelling in the hands and feet. It can be fatal to both mother and child, and preeclampsia is only fixed by the mother giving birth.

She was kept in the hospital for about a month as we monitored her condition. It is miserable for a wife and mother to be stuck in the hospital away from her husband

and children. A month is a long time to be away from home and the duties of home. In our culture, the woman runs the household, and there is guilt associated with being incapacitated from those responsibilities.

We used to make rounds on her morning and evening. It felt like she had become part of our family, we would talk with her, joke with her, and she would tell us the baby names she had picked out.

Finally, the day came when she was going to have an elective c-section. Even before the c-section, with general anesthesia she stopped breathing. We started working to make her breathe again. There were no ventilators at that time; we kept on ambu-bagging her, which is where we use the device to breathe for the patient. It prolongs our ability to give CPR, because the ambu-bag does the breathing by hand, leaving more hands free to pump the heart.

Her husband had made the hard decision to try saving the mom. We did everything possible to save her life. Unfortunately, we lost both. We tried too late to switch our efforts to delivering the baby. There wasn't a dry eye in the surgery room. I remember that as a team, we went to her home and actively participated in her funeral services.

Her husband lost his wife and child that day. There are never words for these situations. We feel helpless and must remember that we have prayed and committed the outcome to God. To this day, I cross the threshold of not speaking about my faith with my patients. It doesn't matter to me where they are in their spiritual life, I know that God guides every move I make, and I give Him the glory for the victories and remind my patients that He is in charge. The outcome is in His hands.

My journey as a doctor has changed from me working with women having babies and beginning families in Pakistan, to nursing home patients in the United States, to primarily my patients at my own practice in internal medicine by this point in my life. Even now, I am transitioning into another role that we will see more of at the end of the book. I share this, because as I write, this is a case that refuses to leave my head.

There is a young woman, Chloe, who was an addict that battled her addictions for a few years. Her family went bankrupt putting her through rehabs and trying to get her to receive the help that she desperately needed to get back to her normal self. Her addictions had started with pain killers, and she eventually ended up on hard street drugs to get the high that she was seeking for. This family fought for her sobriety by being active in her life and involved in her treatments.

Chloe finally became sober after her ICU stay, struggling with life and death due to a K2 overdose. Life was beginning again, and everything should have been perfect from there on out, if she stuck to her sobriety. Then tragedy struck.

Chloe was diagnosed with a brain tumor. She couldn't walk right, and she was losing her mobility in other ways. The brain tumor was progressing quickly, and she had to resort to pain medications for the aches that filled her body. Her family was devastated; their outlook for this 21-year-old young lady was filled with hopes and plans. There were no longer any barriers to her having a successful and fulfilling life, as far as they could tell. Her addiction had held her back at first, and now a brain tumor was holding her back from getting all she could from life, even after going through multiple cycles of chemotherapy, radiation, and various surgeries.

The last time she came to see me, I was shocked at how quickly her condition was worsening. This fueled my frustration with regulations, and I think this, right here, is why people are suffering. Doctors must see patients to prescribe certain medications, even when they are knocking at death's door. Everything in me wanted to beg her family not to bring Chloe in her terminal state. Even though I know they can't help how she is on the day of her appointments, or when they called for an emergency appointment due to their concern, the healthcare provider in me still feels helpless. The rules and regulations surrounding heavy narcotics are to make sure that the drugs aren't being trafficked, so doctors must have eyes on the patient to ensure that they are receiving the medication and that there is a need for it.

There is a huge narcotic problem in the healthcare system, to be sure. There have been patients who were clearly not getting their medicine, because someone was taking it from them and pocketing it. This is especially common when the patient is unable to speak for themselves.

Where do we draw the line? Yes, people become addicted to narcotics, but when they are necessary for a specific patient, we must give them. Once the patient leaves the office, I cannot control where the medications go or end up. It is nothing short of cruel for someone to take necessary medications from someone who needs them. I get so angry for patients that are suffering, and someone wants their narcotics more than they care for their family member. Hospice was not chosen because they were trying so hard to save her, otherwise she would have received comfort care to ease the pain.

This was not happening with Chloe, but it is the reason she had to be brought in, when I knew what she was going through—I had seen her deteriorate, and I wished that others hadn't taken advantage of the system, so I could have made other decisions in her case that would have left her more comfortable at home.

Chloe's family keeps seeking second and third opinions because they are looking for the doctor that will tell them that the tumor is operable. It isn't looking good for her, but my prayers continue on her behalf. I told her the other day, "You can be angry, it would be justified. All the things that you have survived to find yourself in this state. I can't even imagine. There is one other thing that you must realize, that God Almighty knows what He is doing. You must trust that in His plan He has figured out why this suffering must happen. Maybe it will be that you beat this too and go on to help a lot of people. Sadly, you could pass, but we will work to make you comfortable while you and your family seek answers." Until they can grasp this latest calamity to Chloe's health, they will not be able to accept it. Even if they can accept it, it doesn't magically get easier to deal with a terminal illness.

The reason that narcotics are so closely monitored is because people have figured out how to get drugs from multiple providers at the same time. There are patients that are hooked on drugs, and there are those authentically suffering. This may seem revolutionary—but they all need help in their own ways. The highly addicted needs help too, and to ignore their pain is what is killing addicts in droves. Sadly, we cold turkey the wrong patients. Or we don't prescribe enough for people that are suffering. Both sides of this coin toss are a loss. This is where I try to educate my patients and myself to do better for everyone.

My first few patients at my own practice were a husband and wife. He was a good-looking man, always looked far younger than he was. He still played golf as part of a very active lifestyle. He had the shiniest healthy skin; I would comment that I needed his skin regimen so I could have radiant skin like him. He looked like he was in his sixties, despite being much older, and he worked to keep it that way. He would worry about his wife; her weight gain worried him, because of her diabetes. He was concerned that she wasn't taking care of herself, and he loved her.

Every three months, Mr. Blake would come in for blood pressure checks. He would tell me stories about his friends, and go on about his outings, anything not to have to talk about medical concerns.

One day, it was time for a follow-up visit, and we reviewed labs, physical findings, adjusted some meds. We had made it to our fifteen-minute visit time; I made sure to give at least that long. We had covered all the information that I had to review, when he abruptly spoke up as I was turning to leave, "Dr. Noor? By the way, I'm feeling stretching on my side."

Now, in some practices there is a fifteen-minute

cap on doctors visiting in a room. There is a revolving door of patients to ensure maximum income for the practice. I sat back down, "Okay, what's going on?" He started to explain the pulling sensations he was having, so I examined that area only to find that his liver was three to four centimeters below his ribs (the final diagnosis was liver cancer). This had happened between two visits, so in less than three months. Right in front of my eyes, with regular care, something had started to go haywire in his body.

What if I had been part of a practice that penalized me for taking more than fifteen minutes with any given patient? What if I had ushered him out by telling him that I would check at the next visit, a few weeks away? Putting a patient back up on the table for examination takes time. Mr. Blake had liver cancer. That was the official finding, and it was worth going over the fifteen-minute rule. I am glad that I took the time. That was a large motivation to me starting my own practice—I made the rules, and the rules always favored the patients' well-being. It was worth the extra time to listen to Mr. Blake. I took care of him the whole time he was ill, until he passed.

It doesn't matter how many years I have been doing this, when these saddest cases enter my doors, I am still affected by the patients and move through their pain and grief with them. The reality hits: There wouldn't have been a career path that offered more rewards. Seeing people get their lives back is phenomenal and makes it worthwhile to help people through the worst times of their lives.

Of course, there are even more stories of numerous

patients who were diagnosed earlier, stories of cancer in remission, heart attacks prevented, strokes recovered from, but success stories don't stick to the mind like the sad stories.

Recently, I was asked to write an article about compassion, and I am including it here to show that this is something I walk out and share with other doctors: There are experiences that shape our lives. As I consider what defining experiences have made me a better doctor, there is a memory that sticks out that changed how I proceed with my patients and their families in care plans and major treatment decisions.

The memory has to do with the care and treatment of my father. He had been diagnosed with stage four esophageal cancer at only 68-years-old. I wasn't ready to see how pale and severely jaundiced abba jaan (father) was. He looked sad. I only had a few minutes to be with him as my seven-month-old son cries and was sitting in the lobby with my husband and his two sisters, three and five-years-old.

There weren't words as I looked at him. Relief flooded in as he called me to come and sit near him on the bed. He grabbed my hand to hold it and put it on his distended abdomen, full of ascites. His mottled appearance tipped me off to the reality that he was dying. My career in Pakistan was focused on labor and delivery. Time ran out quickly and I wondered if my father would live until I could make it to be by his side again next Saturday.

My father's failing health came on the heels of our migration to the United States. After that first year, I was struggling to become fluent in English while struggling to study for boards. My older sister, a pediatric resident, was the spokesperson for the family. The next morning, she informed me that the doctors wanted to perform a surgical procedure on abba jaan. She had okayed the procedure since he was losing too much albumin with each paracentesis.

I looked at the procedure details (this was before Google and Smartphones) and immediately asked my sister to reverse her decision, as per my last visit he was at the end of life. Putting him through any surgical procedure was not a good idea. I also explained that there are risks with the procedure due to his terminal condition. She requested that I speak to the doctor about my concerns. His cell phone rang, went to voicemail, and I left a message asking him to call me back to discuss my concerns. I ended the message saying that I didn't agree with the surgery. My discomfort with the surgery was not addressed, as I didn't receive a return phone call.

Without my concerns being addressed, my father was wheeled into the operating room against his wishes. My sister saw him resisting and telling them he wasn't willing to get the procedure. His faculties were fully functioning. The procedure was completed and unfortunately, within twenty-four hours, my father had passed away. His death left me filled with guilt and angry with the circumstances.

It became imperative to work harder at passing my boards sooner. My grief became an incredible drive to be the type of doctor that calls concerned family members back. Informed consent hadn't been exhausted in my father's case. Following the wishes of patients and their families became forefront in my growth as a doctor through the experience with my father's death. The inner drive to become the type of doctor my father had needed, that I had needed as a concerned daughter, had me working on my studies throughout the day then staying up until the early hours of the morning, after I had tucked my children into bed for the night. The hard work and prayers paid off with the blessing of being able to practice in the United States.

There are always challenges associated with running a practice and keeping the various patients happy, but I wanted to have open communication channels between myself, the patients, and their concerned family members. There are many times I talk to one family member who refers me to another family member who might have a better understanding of what is going on. When a family presents with varying opinions on the treatment plan for the patient, I work to arrange a meeting with the family members who want to be present to explain any decisions or options. This is my attempt to lessen conflict between the family to resolve differences of opinion. Most of the time, this approach helps families get on the same page through clear explanations. Obviously, if the patient has given verbal or written directives, I will follow those. In the rare cases where there were no arrangements, there were agreements made for consultants can give their input to a case. Rarely, the ethics committee of the hospital had to be involved.

Open communication and explanations coupled

with listening to patients (or their caregivers) is a vital part of practicing medicine. Sitting with patients and listening to them can take longer than the standard fifteen-minute doctor visit. There are times it takes longer to address concerns and fears that patients have. Attempting to address all the concerns can be time consuming, so I have had patients prepare their questions and concerns on a sticky note in order of importance to them. That way, I am covering their biggest issues first, then if there are things that can be visited at a future visit, it won't be forgotten. Most of the time, if we keep our visit focused and organized, we can address the whole list. Active listening helps alleviate apprehension from patients and they tend to leave more content and comforted.

Another commitment I have made from the experience with my father, that I believe makes me a better doctor, is to review all labs and answer all calls before leaving the office. There are days that I leave hours after the last patient has been seen, but people need hope and encouragement in their suffering. My goal is that no daughter, son, or other concerned family member feels that no one listened to their concerns. Accommodating concerns from family members and respecting the sons and daughters who take interest in caring for their families encourages me to push through phone calls and emails to ensure that patients and their families are not overlooked in their times of need.

As doctors, we are affected by personal tragedy, like any other person would be. We aren't exempt from the pain and disappointment of sickness and death. We have choices to make, like anyone else. My father's unfortunate circumstances remind me that while the focus is always the patient and their care, we also have a duty to the family. There are valid concerns that can come from someone who may not be a contact person. It is important to take all concerns into consideration when deciding the correct course of treatment for a patient. Listening was always important to me but losing my father without being heard lit a fire in me to be a better doctor—not just to my patients, but also to and for the people that love my patients.

Chapter Four

The Most Important Secret Skill

The practice of medicine is a religion in which nine out of ten commandments is practicing compassion.

My grandfather was a doctor, and his insights have profoundly affected the way I practice medicine. While he died when I was very young, my abba jaan would share stories about him. One of the things that I heard he always said stuck with me: Compassion and empathy for patients leads to heartfelt prayers that cause patients to be cured, even with only water as medicine. I always took this to mean that the prayers did the healing because the basic elements of compassion and empathy were present.

Once when I was young, my father had a headache, and he sent me to get him a Tylenol. I began to pray for his healing from the pain, and with my whole heart believed that his headache would go away. Later, he mentioned that his headache was gone, so I credited the prayer and the fact that I loved my father enough to pray for him, again, out of compassion and empathy. It was proof positive that my grandfather was on to something that my father felt better such a short while later.

These two secret ingredients go well in the medical profession, in fact, I believe they are vital. Aspects of the provider's personality affect the patients. Compassion brings doctors closer to the patients, which is especially important in times of pain and suffering.

Doctors are set on a pedestal by society. When a disease or accident becomes life or death, it is almost like the doctor is acting in the capacity of God, making decisions to prolong and save life. The doctor then must step into the role of the simple human being and put themselves in the shoes of the patient for personal connection. We call it empathy, more simply. If the doctor must give news to the family—sharing in happiness, sorrow, success, failure, triumph, and mourning—there must be the element of true empathy and understanding.

My goal is to always walk in compassion and empathy with my patients. It has led to a connection with them that goes deeper than just the revolving door, where I go in and see patients and forget them once they have left.

There have been numerous times where I have been so connected to patients in a mental capacity that I have understood that certain patients needed me. Many times, I think of someone specifically and they come in to see me that day or the next. Or, I will have my staff call them to find out how they are doing, even though I have not seen them for any acute medical problems, and my staff informed me that they were on their way, as something wasn't right with them.

Joe and his wife were patients of mine for many years. Once Joe was sick in the hospital, and I happened to see some beautiful flowers in a vase beside him.

"Those are very pretty flowers, Joe," I told him.

Joe beamed up at me, "They are from my garden at home. Thank you."

When he got out of the hospital, at a follow-up visit, Joe brought me a box full of seeds and educated me about the specific flower's needs for planting and care. The next summer, I remembered to plant them. I was on the phone with a friend talking to her about the patient who had given me the seeds I was holding, when I got a call from the emergency room. Joe was there with chest pains.

Another time, I got into the office and thought of Benjamin, so I asked my staff to call him to see how he was doing. They informed me that he had been bitten by a rattlesnake and was recovering from the bite. I was shocked by the severity of his injury, but thankful to God for showing me that I needed to check on him.

Divine help guides me to the right diagnosis which helps save lives. One day, I was following up on a 93-year-old patient, Daphne. Suddenly, I felt like I should examine her breasts. As I checked her, I found a hard lump. I had no reason to think of that, other than God intervened for her and showed me.

Similarly, many times I have been able to diagnose many acute conditions just by examining parts of the body that were not indicated to be examined by the complaints of the patient for that visit.

When I first started my practice, a patient came in that had a black mole on the back of his ear. I asked him if he had seen a dermatologist, and he let me know that he had, and it was fine. I kept urging him to get it checked, and it turned out to be melanoma. In the years since, he has remained in my care, and the trust between us was built by the compassion I had towards a little thing that he hadn't seen as a problem.

As a medical provider, the years I spend with patients is enhanced by compassion and empathy, and I get connected to the patients. Feelings come to my heart that this might be his or her last visit. Sometimes, I get to say goodbye, while other times we just discuss end of life care plans with family members. Even when they are gone, there are times when you can feel the presence of the dead spouse when the living spouse comes for evaluations.

There was another couple that came to the practice, Samuel and Linda. She was twenty years younger than him and in a few visits they became like good friends to me. One day they came to discuss Samuel bleeding after intimacy. We did testing, and he was diagnosed with bladder cancer. Linda being younger became the perfect caretaker, because his condition worsened quickly and dementia set in. His extra care requirements took her full dedication. He was always very appreciative of my care and compassion for him, as was she. We went through the pathway of sickness and at the end of his life, I was there with Linda holding his hand.

Kent was a very active 97-year-old, who was still lived on his farm and took care of his goats. For his age, he was highly functional and intellectual. He would write newsletters to his family. He would bring those newsletters to me, at times. It meant a lot to him that I would read them and discuss the contents at his next visit.

Lenny would bring his wife in to the practice. She had moderate dementia. He would ask every visit if there was any way for me to treat her dementia, to arrest its progress. Unfortunately, there is nothing that can be done once dementia starts moving through its stages. His love for his wife showed in his tenacity to bring up a way to fix her mind each time they were in. It was almost as if he had hoped that there would be new information, and sadly, there are still no significant advances to help dementia and Alzheimer's patients.

Lenny went on vacation to Mexico with his wife, where he died. His wife ended up being placed in a nursing home by the family once they retrieved her from Mexico. They had to travel to get her. I was very sad that this happened. I keep up on these things out of my compassion for my patients. There are doctors who may not remember a name and a chart, but I can recall the details of their lives.

Jenna was another patient I saw empathy and compassion change everything for. She had end stage liver disease due to a fatty liver and was transferred to us from another practice. Jenna was very focused on her disease and would ask multiple questions at every visit. It was sad to watch her cry and worry about her disease. It seemed the only thing that kept her going was tender loving care. My listening to her seemed to build her back up, and I felt helpless, that all I could do was listen and reassure her. Instead of rushing her through a visit, I would schedule her at the end of the day so I could spend extra time with her. She would repeat the same questions and concerns again and again, multiple times. I was forced to respond the same every time since there were no changes. That little gesture made her more at ease and calmed her.

One of my Holocaust survivors was 96 years of age and living alone. She was suffering from many cardiac problems coupled with severe anxiety. She didn't want to take medicine, but she wanted my time, love, attention, and reassurance. She was in the hospital with pulmonary embolisms, and the ER doctors were trying to get her to take blood thinners.

She refused to go on anything without talking to me, so the doctors had to get me on the phone to reassure her that she needed to follow their recommendations. I used to go into the hospitals to take care of my patients, and it helped her so much that I came in to see her as soon as I was available. It wasn't a requirement, but I made the time anyhow.

Now, traditional medicine has given way to hospital doctors taking care of patients at the hospital while primary care physicians take care of patients at the office. There is not the entwinement and working together that there once was. Records get passed back and forth, but the expectation is that the hospital doctors will see to care within the walls of the hospital. I was happy to give that extra care to her. The end of her life was more pleasant just because she had her emotional needs met—which is compassionate care.

When the doctor bonds with patients and their families, the future seems to take on a new light, even after a tragedy. There was an 87-year-old woman who brought her husband in, and on the first visit, he was diagnosed with metastatic lung cancer. He died, and she still comes in regularly to get a hug. She lovingly shares personal memories and thoughts about her grandchildren and great-grandchildren. Her life was able to move forward with hope, because she knew that we cared for her.

Whenever a fellow healthcare professional comes into the practice, there is a natural connection that develops. I have taken care of many nurses and doctors at the end of their lives. We give them the professional curtesy of believing they are still working and performing their duties when dementia sets in, and their minds believe they are working instead of being the patient.

Many people who were active members in society, volunteering all over the town in their social circles, have a difficult time when they end up with dementia. It is hard to watch them lose their driving privileges and their ability move about freely—it's very humbling.

Compassion and empathy aren't just for the patient. Caregivers need tremendous amounts of support and understanding in their duties. Education plays an important role in sharing compassion, easing the stress of colleagues who are dealing with life and death daily. If there isn't a healthy outlet being expressed, doctors can slip into depression or hopelessness. Of course, these are the little secrets of the trade. Doctors must maintain their professional appearances, but we all need empathy and compassion being shown to us as we walk our paths in life, even doctors.

It has been my experience that the patient can start feeling better just by talking with their doctor. Paying attention to their concerns and fears while holding their hand seems to make all the difference. The secret ingredients to this profession are compassion and empathy.

Chapter Five

Duty:
Pathway to Success

Medicine is genderless, raceless, and should embrace the patient, regardless of lifestyle choices.

Going through medical school in Pakistan, then two residencies and internships in two different countries was challenging. Passing the boards initially in each country was a journey to duty all on its own. There were great memories, to be sure, but duty drove me.

When a person commits their life to serving others, the inner drive to that end becomes a consuming force. My prayer life confirmed that I was going in the correct direction. God puts into people's hearts the things that He has designed for them. It was only His grace that saw me through. None of the tasks set ahead of me were easy, but they have all proved worth it.

One of my earlier memories was when everyone was sick in the house with the flu. My sister, who was six-years-old at the time, is going from one person to another with a thermometer saying, "I am the doctor in the house." This is a memory from when I was three-years-old. My older sister was on her way; everyone called her 'doctor,' and she was the smart one. No one doubted that she would become a doctor, she knew from a very early age that she aspired to the role of doctor.

There were eight of us, brothers and sisters, raised

in a small town. Our mother did not allow us to wear heels when we were little. We always dreamed of wearing nice heels that make noise when you walk. When the health visitor came to assist my mother with the birth of our younger sister, we were enamored of the clicking of her heels. This is coming up again, because it helped shape who I have become.

It is funny how little things like the way a woman's heels click when she walks can affect a young child. This thought drives me to be someone that young girls look up to in their quest to discover what they may do in the future. The impact that health visitor had on me was huge, and I want any impact I might have on another person to leave positive thoughts and inspire them.

All through my childhood I never worked hard on anything but my faith. My inner drive was for a relationship with God and was my sole focus. Of course, I always did my homework. I was in the top ten percent of my class, while my older sister was always in the top one percent. I thought she was the smart one, and I didn't want to compete, so I never thought that I should work hard to become the top one percent. What was the point? My sister had already accomplished it and gotten attention for it. I was happy to pray and do what I wanted, maintaining my top ten percent ranking.

It is laughable to remember that I would play all day and just finish my homework as quickly as possible. It seems I never cared. Maybe I was being saved time early on since the boards would take all my time studying later in life. I informed my whole family that I would stop my education after high school. There was no clear direction behind that decision, it just seemed to be the answer for me at the time.

When I noted that I was in the top five percent when graduating from high school, I felt encouraged, thinking that if I can be top five percent without working hard, then hard work could easily bring me up to top one percent, like my older sister.

At that time my older sister had already started medical school, and I was starting pre-med. Whenever she came home from school, we all sat around her while she told us stories of dissecting human bodies and many other interesting things from medical school. As she told her stories, my brain started building the next door that I would walk through.

I decided to start working harder. Abba jaan was out of the country; therefore, I was not allowed to go to any college outside of my town. I started pre-med education in my hometown, since it was my only local option. We did not have professors of biology and chemistry, so we had to do self-study. Self-study is not easier than taking a class—there is no one to explain what you are reading to you. Instead of being easier, it was more of a challenge.

The other challenge is motivating yourself to set apart the time to do the work. It is very easy to get distracted and focus on what seems like more pressing matters. Scheduling time every day, on top of the normal schoolwork and responsibilities, was important for success. Biology and chemistry are vital to studying medicine, so it wasn't like these two courses could be put on the backburner and done half-heartedly. That would have been a foolish thing to do, and with my determination and knowing God's expectations of my best being put forth, I buckled in and excelled even in the self-study courses. He gave me the strength to push through the exhaustion and disappointment of the time commitment that I had made. There were times that I wished I were free to pursue other things. I wouldn't let my mind wander for too long, to keep myself from being distracted from my obligations.

There was a male professor who would come to teach female students when we got into more difficult levels of biology and chemistry. I elected to focus on the self-study once again, since I had been successful completing the other courses. I had learned what was needed to excel, so it seemed natural to take the responsibility on again. It seemed easier to continue with the schedule that I had already created with the added benefit of requiring no travel, so that made life easier.

We were always in full dress, hijab, while our professor was on the stage teaching. Our community and town boasted a majority of the people from our sect. The migration from India to Pakistan had helped us all settle in together. Upon migrating to Pakistan, the community had bought the whole town, for the purposes of us practicing our faith freely.

The Ahmadiyya sect was severely persecuted due to our belief in the Messiah that was born in India in 1835. Muhammed had prophesied that the Messiah would come 1,400 years after His death to revive the faith, since people would forget the original Islam.

In 1974, the leaders of the country said we weren't Muslims because we believed in the Messiah. This is an aside, but an interesting one: Our new town began under our administration in 1948, which meant that all the rules and regulations were made by our administration. The people of our sect migrated to Pakistan, as we had an area in the subcontinent that we were given to purchase in Punjab. The people coming from India were given the chance to purchase comparable lots of land in Pakistan. This piece of barren land was developed into a beautiful town under the guidance of our leader. Our sect funded our own schools and colleges for men and women separately, so we could have teachers from our sect. The highly focused education and high standards led to our students placing in the top positions in the country boards.

In 1974, the leaders of the country said we weren't Muslims because we believed in the Messiah. Well, that went south when the government took control of our schools. The schools in our town became dormant, because teachers and professors wouldn't come there any longer. The town would see them begrudgingly show up, stay for three to four months and then leave as quickly as they had come. Our tenacity as a community saw us through and we managed to still accomplish all our goals. We didn't give up. That has been the foundation of my faith since I was young. There were always threats to our safety, but our trust in God was stronger than any outside intimidation.

My mother was a constant in my life, especially with my father being away a lot with his duties as a missionary. My siblings and I would sleep in her bed with her, since my father was gone. I observed her closely. She cared for me in my sickness with extreme love and affection. I was quiet natured, and she would give me special attention. She always made sure we had the correct nutrition, even though there wasn't a lot of money. She was rock solid, raising all of us, caring for our home, making sure that we focused on our prayers and faith first and our studies second. Mother guided us and her dedication to our family and home ensured that we have all had successful lives. All her children were blessed by her diligence and love.

When my father was back home, he always motivated and encouraged my hard work. He woke me up early in the morning with a nutritious drink called HARIRA. This was a drink made with cream of wheat and sugar that he mixed to help us feel satiated and keep our focus. It is quite possible that the 'science' behind it working was the fact that it was something special that abba jaan did for us. This was his encouragement for any of his children that were taking exams.

Father advised me to wake up and study, as early morning brain is fresher and can understand, taking in more information with higher retention rates of new knowledge. At first, I thought he was just trying to motivate me, but then my brain started firing on an increased level. This is when I learned to admit that listening to my father was paramount to my success. He would talk to me about my studies, challenging me with the wisdom he had gained over a lifetime. 'What-if' scenarios were his favorite to throw at me to check my problem-solving skills.

"What if you encounter a patient with…" and he

would name some extreme condition and symptoms.

There were a few times that I chuckled and said, "Abba jaan, surely I will not encounter a situation such as you have described."

"My dear daughter," he would start, "what have you seen of the world? We have left you in the comfort of familiarity, meaning you have lived a moderately safe life with stable experiences. This is not the case for all others. Just down the road someone might be starving. There is violence that takes lives, and you hear about it. Don't you think as a doctor you might begin to see it?"

There are some things in life that leave you speechless, and this moment was one of those for me, as I contemplated the truth he had just dumped into my lap.

What was I signing up for in life? Had I really thought this through? There could be horrid things showing up needing my care, was I up for the task? Looking back, I know that these concerns are normal. Human beings never know what they are capable of until they are challenged. That's when you hear of superhuman feats like a mother lifting a car off her child. You hear of people snapping and taking a life when all their closest friends and relatives are saying, "They were the nicest, calmest, kindest person you could ever meet."

Life happens. It happens in ways that are not logical or fair. As I considered what abba jaan had ju st opened my heart and eyes to, I knew to pray, but I became firmer in my resolve to be a doctor. If I could just save one, I thought, I would be doing my duty.

My father was writing the life history of his father in those days. Whenever I passed by him, I heard stories from my grandfather's life. He was a physician and had worked in the jungles of Indonesia. My aunt, my father's sister, had told me stories from his life. He served humanity in the true sense, by giving up his homeland and the people that looked and spoke like him, to save the lives of people he had never met and who could not benefit him. He was there to help them with no strings attached.

After an entire day's work in the clinic and hospital, he would come home to have dinner with his family. Many of these days, there would be a knock at the door from someone begging him to go see a sick family member at their home. Grandfather would take his bag and oil lantern and follow into jungles, on foot, even though the trek could take him miles and hours away. When he would go look at the household situation of the family, he would come back home without taking any money in exchange for his services, and sometimes he would donate some money to the poor family for medications. His life was one of active and continuous sacrifice.

This made me study harder, so that I could be in the same situation as my dear grandfather. The goal was to be able to help people, without any reservations or without any limitations. That was my new focus. There is a quiet strength to having the ability to help another human being, in their weakest state, knowing that they cannot give anything in return, except for giving of their life and time because they have more of it. Doctors have the special ability to catch things and know how to treat them, it's a gift. The studying and sacrifice on the way to becoming a doctor is to serve people when they need it most.

In this way, I knew I could help humanity. The idea of selfless giving became a strong motivator for me. The sense of duty stirred me to stay the course, but amazingly also grew. If I had known then where life would take me in my capacities as a doctor, all the complaints that cropped up from time to time would have been buried in the sense of purpose my younger self would have drawn from knowing. As I reflect, I can see that God knew my heart and reflected my wildest dreams back to me in the form of a fulfilling career.

I was very motivated and wanted to succeed. But first, I had to enter medical school. In those days, we did not have any private medical schools. Getting into national medical schools was extremely difficult. You had to be the top three to five percent in the country, then there was a chance that you would be considered for medical school applications. Even if we had a private medical school, my family would not have been able to afford the cost of private medical school. There were too many kids in our home to afford private schools for all of us. Plus, there were two of us working to become doctors. We had to make it in the top of our class!

My daily routine was to wake up between four and five in the morning, offer prayers, then study for an hour or two. Once I finished that, it was time to make breakfast for the whole family and get ready for school. After school and lab studies, I would walk alone to a chemistry professor for lessons, about two miles away from school. He was a very nice elderly professor, a friend of my father, he always liked my understanding of organic chemistry.

After taking chemistry lessons, I would come home between seven and eight p.m., another two and a half miles of walking. It seemed burdensome at the time. I hesitate to share this memory, but it proves that I was always looking for ways to test my knowledge and skills. In my biology class I was told that we would be dissecting a frog. I was very excited and had a dissection box. For some reason, I decided to try it even before the class got a chance to participate in the experience.

I had an empty can of Ovaltine on hand and went out to the garden. Luckily for me, I quickly found a small frog, closed it in the can, then went to the pharmacy to get ether. My younger brother was with me. Both of us sprayed ether in the can, which was more than enough to make the frog sleepy. He was out.

I put him on the dissection board and opened his abdomen gently. Mesmerized when I saw the heart beating and all the organs, I missed that the ether may have been wearing off. Suddenly, the frog woke up and started running around the room!

My brother and I were running after him with the can. Finally, he was in the can again, and we gave him a little more anesthesia and sutured him with my mother's sewing needle. After sewing him back together, he woke up again and started jumping. I took him back to the garden and set him down, hoping for the best.

When I went to check on him the next day, he was there, still breathing and seemingly none the worse for the wear. So, this frog was technically my first patient.

The good news is he survived, and I was unable to locate him after the first day, so that is the end of my report on the little frog's life, my first patient. I still laugh to speak of it.

That experience was life changing because I didn't perform the dissection on a dead animal but was able to see his organs pumping and working. I learned how important trained anesthesiologists are to surgery. Maybe, the take-home lesson was the realization that I could do this, that the blood and guts wouldn't bother me. A new confidence followed my studies after this experience.

The hard work of getting up earlier than everyone and going to bed long after everyone else had drifted into dreamland, to ensure my studies were done, was fruitful. When it was time for the results of the national test, I went into hiding because I was scared about the outcome. When I worked up the nerve to see the notice board, I was looking through the list and could not find my name! I was getting nervous, my heart beating fast trying to jump out of my chest.

My dreams could die right here if I didn't make the marks. It took confidence to look at the top of the list, and there I was. I had achieved the highest grade in my school. That moment became a time of thanksgiving to God for giving me the strength and willpower to keep going, even when I was tired or felt like there was something else I would rather be doing.

I started applying to medical schools. I even applied to army medical school; I liked the way the army doctors would dress up in khaki Saris. The results of matching for army medical school came before civil medical schools. I was not accepted; my father called me in private and advised me that he did not want to see me sad or crying over this failure, as there is always a good reason behind it. Sometimes it is hard to see that there may be a reason when there is a disappointment.

Had I joined the army, my path would not have turned out the same as it is now. Perhaps, that rejection has saved my life. Either way, the ability to run my own practice has left the way I run the office in my hands. Prayer is central to my practice, and it is my belief that it should be more widely accepted and utilized, without fear.

I will share my concept of acceptance of prayers. There are scientific studies that prove that prayer works in the field of medicine. Stephen W. Crawford, MD, in an article titled, "Prayer in the ICU," determined that, out of over 200 patients interviewed, almost half of the patients wanted their doctors to pray for them. Almost 70% had never had their physician discuss religious beliefs. That's a huge jump, showing that more people wish their doctors would pray than have even been talked to about faith.

There's more. The article lists the effects of prayer that were noticed during a different study. There are six listed, but I will just share a few: improved recovery from surgery, lower blood pressure, improved mental health, along with better heart effects. There was a control study about the effects of prayer on coronary patients and the patients that were prayed for fared better than their peers—in EVERY area of study.

Ultimately, I share all of this here to say that prayer

works, and it has always worked. I prayed while I waited for an acceptance letter, and I committed in my prayers to be a praying doctor. My heart understood, by faith, that there was something different with praying physicians. I will tell you that some things are understood divinely and don't need proof (although the proof is interesting and rewarding to have).

Waiting for acceptance to the program that starts a career is a lot like torture. I hadn't planned for anything else. There wasn't a backup plan or option. The longer I had to wait for a letter from medical school, it seemed the more my heart sank. My mind was unable to fathom that failure could be an option. My heart and soul had gone into being the best student and my marks had shown that I had excelled above my peers.

Surely, I was going to medical school. There was a lesson in the waiting. God was showing me to have patience, and it was not an easy lesson to learn.

Chapter Six

The Journey Begins

Caring for those in distress is an act of charity.

A few months later, I was accepted to medical school. This was a very big achievement for me, but my father called me and advised me that I should consider not going to medical school due to my allergies, asthma, and all these minor illnesses I struggled with. His concern was that I would not be able to take the load of all the necessary studies.

Inside, the assurance was that I had already excelled to be at the top of my class, so I knew I could handle all the classes and work. That wasn't my concern. His protective reasoning made sense, but it wouldn't stop me.

The second reason was that he couldn't afford the cost of two daughters in medical school at the same time. My older sister was in her fourth year of medical school, and medical school isn't cheap. When he voiced this concern, I started crying and said, "No abba jaan, I want to go to medical school." His heart was broken. Of course, he wanted me to be able to go, but the meager income he acquired in missionary work was not enough to send multiple children to medical school. My older sister and I were not the only ones with plans to go to college.

During those days, there was an examination

announced for the religious education of the girls in our town. The girl who scored highest was supposed to get a one-time scholarship of 500 rupees. I decided to study hard for the exam and scored at the top! They awarded me the scholarship of 500 rupees. This was a big amount for me.

That night I had a dream and saw that there was a woman in the servant quarters of my high school who needed some money. The next day, I went to her house and donated a small amount of money to the lady. I wasn't concerned about provision. This scholarship had been a gift from God. Deep down, I knew that my obedience would reap rewards beyond what I had available in my hands now.

Giving is a way of receiving when our hearts are in the right place. It didn't feel like enough; I still did not feel satisfied. I had read in the Holy Quran, and other religious books, that if you spend out of what you have, the money in your hands gets multiplied up to 700-fold. Therefore, I decided to go to the president of the Women's Organization and donate another small portion of my scholarship money.

My trust in God was such that I knew that He would supply all my needs. Surely, He had answered my prayers to win the scholarship, to get me closer to realizing my goals of being a doctor when the odds seemed stacked against me. If I would continue being faithful in my prayers while doing what was asked and expected of me, then God would make sure that my needs were met. This was a fact to me, not an idea or wishful thinking.

The money left was about 300 rupees, I took it with me to be deposited in a bank near my medical school. Being careful with money was in my nature, and while 300 rupees doesn't seem like a lot to some, I knew how to stretch it in these circumstances. Although, I would much rather have enjoyed the money, I knew it had to last.

Medical school was in a city about one hour away from my hometown but traveling conditions in the buses were not safe for women and girls to travel daily, so I had to stay at the campus. The cost of staying in the dorm, with education and books, was about 4,000 rupees every year.

My father advised me to go meet a very noble person in our town, and he advised me to apply for another scholarship. Without help, my education was not going to come to fruition. I was qualified to get that grant, and that's how I was able to start my studies. I thanked God profusely for his provision and guidance on the financial matters. I made a promise to God, out of my gratitude, to help a poor student as soon as I was able to give in that way.

The first day of medical school was another experience! All these boys were coming and interviewing the girls, asking them funny questions and making them feel embarrassed. I was from a town where there was complete sexual segregation; we had not talked to boys, and I used to wear ubaya and a hijab on my face, leaving me in total anonymity to the boys, completely modest, according to the standards that were expected.

Dealing with their questions was very difficult

for me, but God gave me strength and courage to answer their questions politely, because if you did not answer, they would tease you more. We were called 'first year fools.' There was no prior preparation or expectation of this abuse and behavior. Males in our community did not behave this way toward females, and while it was shocking, it did prepare me for some of the people that I would encounter later in life and as a doctor.

My first day at the dorm, it became clear that they assigned four girls to one large room. The dormitory of girls, for the actual medical school, was under construction, so we were assigned to the dormitory of the agricultural university, next to the school. All the other girls were from different cities and villages; some of them were more outgoing than others. They all decided to go out for dinner and to go shopping every so often. As I did not have much money on me, I told them I did not feel good, and I was not going with them. When they left, I spent all the time that they were gone crying in my bed. I was missing home and feeling sad for not being able to go socialize like the others were able to do.

It seemed such a big deal then, but I know now that I really didn't miss much. It seems that people who aren't as fortunate as others seem to think that they are missing out on life when they are unable to do the things that they see others doing, but there are things that we miss out on that ends up being good for us that we missed the experience. For instance, how fickle is it to think that things are more important than people? Or how silly is it to spend money on luxuries, to keep up appearances with other people, and be unable to pay for necessities? People in America call it 'keeping up with the Joneses.'"

I was taught not to go into debt, and it is something that my husband and I have consistently held to. Yet, in America, people amass incredible amounts of debt for education, homes, vehicles, and they must work to pay bills for things they can't afford to impress people that may not even think of them. It seems counterproductive to the 'American Dream' of prosperity and wealth, yet it is pervasive. It wasn't always so different in Pakistan, other than we didn't have debt opportunities. If you didn't have the money, you couldn't have 'it,' whatever 'it' may be.

The trend, here in America, is to strive for the 'American Dream.' A lot of people get trapped into debt by buying things to their capacity (do you really need thirty-seven purses?). Once you need to obtain so much stuff, the use of credit cards comes in handy, until you're enslaved by them. Then you can only afford to pay the interest, because there are multiple cards maxed. Pretty soon, there is no way out of the debt hole. My husband and I call it the 'revolving door of debt.'

Once you are walking through the revolving door of debt, you're always broke, working to pay bills, and there is no freedom. Why is this relevant? Because I have seen doctors get stuck in the cycle. A higher income doesn't ensure good money management.

Money should serve you, not the other way around. Mastering the concept of money is a means to an end. This is a core thing that my husband and I stand on together in agreement, and it has made all the difference in our adult life.

That is why my father was so intent on helping me

to obtain the funds for my education, thinking outside of the box to make sure that I was able to remain in school. All these circumstances never made me feel less fortunate. My parents had brought us up in a very dignified manner; we never asked anyone for help, but spent our time living within our means. My father had multiple master's degrees, but he had dedicated his life to the service of our community. Because of his choice to forsake a lucrative career for spreading God's love, he only received a small amount as a stipend with which to raise eight children. God always provided. He is faithful. There wasn't always a ton of money for extras, but we were happy, and we loved each other.

As soon as I started studying anatomy and physiology, I felt like my brain was made for this. Everything from anatomy, physiology, histology to microbiology was very appealing to me! It seemed my neurons would fire and connect time and again. I got fascinated to see the structure of a heart, the valves and chordae tendineae, little tendons that tie up heart valves to the heart muscles, help the valves to close or open.

I went to the butcher's shop and bought a heart, a kidney, and an eye. My tenacity for studying the way things worked went outside of the classroom. Focus and drive led me to the sense of duty that I cultivated toward my fellow human beings, as I realized how amazingly our Creator had constructed us. The burning desire to be a doctor, that had grown in me, was the love of God for others, and He had set within me the ability to learn these amazing things and retain the information. He had blessed me with a stomach that could deal with the inner workings of the human body and all the fluids that came from or resided behind the epidermis.

When I cut the eye from the butcher shop, a button like structure fell out of it along with water; that was the lens. My journey made it so I could not stop appreciating the beauty and wisdom God has shown in each little part of the body. Knowing anatomy and physiology brought me closer to God. It was amazing. Appreciation and awe grew in me as my knowledge increased. There was an additional realization that was humbling—that with all I was learning, it didn't scratch the surface of all there was to know with the variations of animals and uniqueness of each human being.

I remember when I was learning anatomy and physiology of the larynx, I took cardboard and made the model of the larynx that would demonstrate how the epiglottis, the lid of the voice box, covers the voice box when we swallow and how food slides down on it to enter the food pipe. There are so many mechanics and intricate details in what seems like the simplest movements of the human daily routine, and this only made me bow down in front of the Musawir, the Designer, an attribute of God.

Dysphagia was interesting to me. It is where the patient has trouble swallowing. Most people experience dysphagia after a stroke, with dementia, or because of another catastrophic event. In normal people, the air pipe is in front of the food pipe. When we swallow, the epiglottis covers the air pipe and prevents food from entering the air pipe. This is accomplished by the movement of all the tiny muscles that work to bring the epiglottis over the airway. For stroke and dementia patients, these muscles stop working and food goes into the airways causing pneumonia. This makes a huge difference in people's lives. Even though it's such a simple process, everything changes once this functioning breaks down.

The patient will now need pureed food; water needs to be gelatinous, like pudding, for the patient to be able to drink. Now that I'm a practicing doctor, I can tell you, it hurts me to see that! How difficult has life become when patients can't even enjoy a glass of water? Next, comes feeding tubes.

We must monitor even when the patient swallows their own saliva, as they could choke. It is hard to imagine how much saliva we swallow every day or how many swallowing movements we do in an hour. For patients with dysphagia, when they swallow the saliva goes down the airway. Saliva contains a lot of bacterium so when going down wind pipes it could cause pneumonia, choking, and/or suffocation. The hidden mechanics of the body, that work without our involvement, are intricately designed and amazing. Watching them breakdown with age and disease is difficult for healthcare providers. Many times, there is not much we can do to repair such disruptions. We can only treat the symptoms for comfort. Many people don't even recognize that this can happen, let alone how detrimental and awful it is. Modern medicine doesn't have an easy fix for everything. We can rig things to sort of work, with an error margin, but the Creator didn't make mistakes. Our bodies will break down over time and with age, but we are intricately knit together in perfection and nothing of our bodily functioning is simple. There is a lot of connection, and that is true for every area of life.

All these extra activities were not required of me, as part of my assignments, but I wanted to learn and understand to then educate all the other girls in my dormitory. My motivation was not often paralleled by my peers. They would take their time off, while I plunged forward into side projects to make sure that I was grasping every possible piece of information. We would learn about a structure in a book, and I would go to the butcher and examine what we were learning on my own cadaver pieces.

The more I studied medicine, I felt my brain was opening. Every day I was helping my classmates understand anatomy and physiology better, due to my ambition. I would walk outside my dorm with my friend and recite the anatomy of the whole body without looking at the book. There was a sense of pride that came with the ability that God was growing in me, and I made sure to give Him the glory.

From the very beginning, I said that I would become an internist. I remember entering the dissection hall for the first time, the smell of formaldehyde stopped me from opening my eyes. There was this body on the dissection table and fifty students were assigned to it. I was used to the scent of raw blood from animals killed for food, but not this chemical scent in a closed room.

Twenty-five boys on the right side of the body and twenty-five girls on the left side of the body made tight quarters to work in. We were all vying for space, trying to learn skin, muscles, nerves, and blood vessels. The strangest part was dealing with male genitalia, it was more than awkward. While dissecting the groin area, boys would push it towards the girls while girls pushed it back towards the boys. In the evening, this was the topic of discussion and laughter amongst the girls in the dorm.

After that first dissection, that very same night, I kept on thinking about the person who was on the table. He had a childhood, an adulthood, and now he seemed to be about sixty. One day, he might be going out to take care of his children and family and his life ended; maybe he was homeless and had no family; nevertheless, his sacrifice was a source of learning for all the students who would most likely be serving numerous other human beings in the future.

We were told that most of the bodies that we got in medical school were of those who were homeless with no one to claim their bodies. This information was not for sure, it was the gossip amongst the students. Either way, whether he was homeless or had donated his body to science, it was a sacrifice that served others. Someone had loved this person on the table at some point in his life, and we were using the body in a sterile and disconnected way—no emotions for the person, just the scientific sterility of learning, so that one day we could serve the living. It was sad, but necessary.

The first year of medical school meant being harassed by second, third, fourth, and final year students. This ritual didn't make a ton of sense to me. Why was there a need to harass and demean future colleagues and doctors? In my mind, it was counterproductive to future collaborations. How were we to respect the same people who put us down and made fun of us in an emergency when we could remember their unkind words from school?

Girls were assigned to sit in the front rows of the bus when we had to ride one, and boys were supposed to sit in the back. Some of the students would stay in medical school for years. They would not pass the boards but would harass girls and make fun of girls to intimidate them when riding the bus. The bus would pick us from our dorm to drop us at school and to the hospitals, or other places we needed to go for our learning. They would sing funny songs and make rude comments. The girls never confronted them and ignored their comments, hoping that they would just give up in their cruelty.

There were 300 people in our class, out of them only thirty-one were girls and the rest were boys. This was a mixed school; there were also two schools only for ladies, but this was closer to home and more affordable, since it wasn't a private college, and I was matched here.

Girls were assigned seats on the left side in the front in the lecture hall, the rest of the seats were for boys. Out of the thirty-one girls, there were only ten of us in the dorm. We were very close to each other. Whenever anyone had any difficulty understanding anything, they would come to me, the bookworm that took on extra work. I would make a demonstration of the topic and explain in detail. That helped them and it also helped me, even more, to understand the topic.

I belonged to the sect of Islam that was persecuted in the country. When there were riots against our sect in the country, people became angry and would bang on my door and harass me. They would stop talking to me and would not make any eye contact. But after the trying time was over, they would be friendly again, as if nothing had happened. Those periods of unrest may have been the strangest part for me. My faith was so strong, that I would post Quranic scriptures and prayers outside my door, which could have landed me in prison since we were deemed non-Muslims. Passersby would rip down what I posted, and I would just post them again the next day. There were people posted at the school just to cause issues, they weren't even students. It is interesting to look back and realize how brave I was at that time.

During the rioting times, other students would have objections about the girls from our sect eating meals in the main dining room, as they spread fear that we would make the dining room unclean. The cook used to serve us meals in our rooms. This was extremely helpful to us during examinations, as we didn't have to leave our books and could eat while studying, then after eating we just had to put dishes outside the room for kitchen people to pick up. Inside, I would be thankful for the chance to study more with less wasted time—there was no waiting for food, killing precious time, just a knock on the door, a tray brought in, and the ability to work while we ate!

One of the girls from our sect would take me down to the dining room, before dinner time, and we would touch all the dishes secretly. As they continued to say that we were non-believers and we were unclean, the other students didn't want to eat at the same table with us. There is a wrong interpretation of Quranic verses in mainstream Muslims that leads to misguidance and discrimination of non-Muslims. No one is unclean; all people should be respected and have their rights. Instead of gracing them with our presence at dinner, we would go down, touch all the dishes before they came to eat to make them 'unclean.' Sometimes we would giggle, but I didn't feel too awful about it, because we were not unclean—we were observant praying Muslims. We would giggle and pray that the violence and hatred would end.

The division just made us easy scapegoats, an excuse for others to be angry at fellow human beings, instead of trying to fully understand the problems around us. Being on the side that was persecuted, I wonder about the motivations of the persecutors. Did they really believe that their outward show of hatred was accomplishing something? Did their aggression and unkind words make them feel satisfied in some way? Was there ever any guilt for their actions? What was the motivation for their behaviors?

This lack of tolerance and non-acceptance of differences is the cause of restlessness and disputes in the world. So many innocent souls get killed and there is so much bloodshed in the world because people do not accept differences. We don't give every individual the right to live the way they want. The world is at the brim of war which will cause massive destruction in lives.

The discrimination against our sect wasn't going to fix any of the problems, in fact, it just made life more difficult for everyone. Hatred isn't the answer, especially when it is aimed at people that keep God's laws and are fervent in prayer.

The first two years of medical school consisted of theoretical education followed by the last three years of clinical medical education and clinical rotations. This is where med school became very interesting! It seemed it was easier to learn and understand new information, most likely because it was hands-on learning.

In the morning, we had lectures. Then in the afternoon, we made rounds, called clinical rotations.

One of the conditions that we saw early on and has stuck with me from that time is rheumatic heart disease, which results from streptococcal infection of the throat followed by antibody formation. These antibodies can settle on heart valves and damage them. This was very common; we saw very young girls with mitral valve stenosis (tightening of the one of the valves of the heart, that results in congestive heart failure).

We did not have facilities to do testing by echocardiogram; we only had the ability to make the diagnosis by patient history and physical examination. We used to perform all the different maneuvers. There is a reliance on machine testing in the Western world that is almost frightening. The reliance on test results takes the personal care aspect out of medicine and healthcare.

Doctors use great judgment when taking care of patients. The challenge is that there are many symptoms that present in various illnesses. For example, both the flu and an infection can have a fever. If it is flu season, and you have not told the doctor about an injury such as having metal cut deep into your skin, it is possible that the flu could be the first culprit in the doctor's mind, instead of the possibility of an infection. That is why it is so important for the patient to share all symptoms and concerns with the doctor, answering all the doctor's questions, so the correct treatment plan can be put in place.

We were forced to come up with the diagnosis, whether it was a tight valve or leaky valve; we had to figure out which valve was involved. I have never forgotten the thin built bodies of young patients, with their hearts beating out of their chest walls. It was easy to diagnose that their hearts were significantly enlarged. Then we would confirm with the attending doctor.

I remember in our orthopedic rotation, our attending talked in a very monotonous voice, and his rounds were in the afternoon, when everyone already felt sleepy. It is humorous to remember, he put an x-ray on the screen and started speaking in his monotonous voice, "This is an x-ray. This is a chest x-ray. What is wrong with this patient?"

When no one answered right away, he continued, "What is wrong with this x-ray? What is wrong in the lungs? And what's going on with the heart? Look at the ribs." He would ask all these questions in his monotonous voice.

We were only half-awake, trying to look at this x-ray. He seemed to expect an immediate answer from the brightest and best students, but we stared at him blankly, expectantly. After about ten minutes, he would answer, "This is a normal x-ray." Since his tone and intonation never changed, we hadn't been sure what we were looking for, but I know I was glad that I had stayed silent and hadn't overanalyzed the x-ray.

During my gynecology and obstetrics rotation, my first exposure to a natural birth was horrifying. It was the birth of a stillborn. The mom was screaming so loud! It was incredibly scary; that picture got imprinted in my brain: A mother's pain bearing a child who is not alive. Her happiest moment turned into mourning, as she felt every pain of labor only to go home with empty arms. This was a scarring first encounter with childbirth.

The ladies were brought from villages; they screamed loudly. In labor, that was the norm. They didn't have any education of what to expect in a normal labor, how to breathe. Even I learned about breathing through labor, and had a positive image of childbirth, even though I was electing to have a C-section, so I didn't have to take the classes. There were no epidurals available at that time. Oh, how medicine has changed. The women would scream at the top of their lungs, cursing their husbands; it was not a pleasant experience at all.

Husbands were not allowed to come inside to listen to all these curses. They got to stay home or in the lobby until the baby was born.

I got married at the end of my fourth year in medical school, and in the last five months of my final year, I was pregnant with my first child. As soon as I saw the positive pregnancy test, I started thinking of those horrific stories which scared me to death; I started crying (I had thought it was a good idea to have a child after final year and before starting residency).

At the time of graduation, I was five months pregnant and the rest of the pregnancy, I was home with my husband.

During my last trimester, I was scared. If I didn't feel the movement of the baby, I would start crying and become scared of having a stillborn. This experience of childbirth during my clinical rotation caused very negative images of delivery. I had requested a c-section, as all my sisters had c-sections. I asked this not knowing the details of a c-section and what it entails.

My gynecologist wrongly decided to induce me at thirty-eight weeks, when the cervix was not effaced at all. The contractions lasted for three days. On the morning of the fourth day, I took a wheelchair and started walking out of the labor ward. When the attending physician saw me leaving the labor ward he ran up and asked, "Where are you going?"

I explained that I would like to have a c-section, as I was exhausted from three days of contractions. My biggest concern was that I would not be able to push, and I did not want to have my child with the use of forceps. Finally, I was in the OR (operating room) waiting to have a c-section. When the attending physician came, I requested horizontal incision. I did not want a midline vertical incision. Things went well, and little Sehar was born, pretty and loudly screaming, letting me know that she was very much alive after her birth.

Natural birth has multiple benefits. When the child is born the chemicals are released from the body causing bonding and love between the mother and child. Now, when I experience my grandchildren being born, there is the concept of skin-to-skin contact that was not practiced in those days. I had general anesthesia, so I missed the first cries. The after effects of C-sections are much more complicated when compared to a natural birth. A woman's body heals faster, and she is better able to care for her child when she is not dealing with the healing process from a surgery.

After the c-section, the next day, knowing basic medical knowledge, I decided that if I was up and getting about sooner, I would protect myself from blood clots in my legs and lungs. I knew that I would recover faster, so I told my husband to help me get out of the bed and sit in the chair. Due to not knowing how to protect my abdominal muscles when getting out of bed, I had the most severe pain of my life! I felt like I was ripping apart, from the inside out, that scared me to death! I decided that I should not get out of my bed at all.

Here I was, in the bed, for five days. Finally, the doctor's team came and made an announcement that they were there to make me walk. I had to walk that day no matter what. So, they made me get out of bed and took me for a walk all around in the ward. They took me to another room, where another doctor had not walked for seven days after a natural birth proving "doctors and nurses make the worst patients." I felt proud of myself for getting out of the bed in five days. That made me encouraged, and I was discharged home.

This began my days of studying with a newborn. Luckily, my mother-in-law was there to help me. I want to mention my gratitude for how fortunate I am to have such a nice mother-in-law. She sacrificed her night's sleep for my children, they slept with her. She woke during the night to change their diapers and feed them. I was at the hospital, which made me feel like I wasn't responsible enough to be a mother until my last child, my son, was born, who I took care of alone. I was able to run my household, take care of Sehar, and work on studying, all while planning for my residency.

Remember the 300 rupees that I started medical school with, from the scholarship? I wanted to share here that those 300 rupees that I deposited in an account, near my medical school, were so blessed that I never ran out of money. My account was never empty. Even my roommate, who belonged to a very rich landlord, would ask me for loans. And up until my final year, there was always money in that account. That was a true blessing from God that I always thanked Him for.

Chapter Seven

Internal Medicine Residency and Hardships

SUCCESS is:
Determination + Hard Work +Dedication =
Blessings multiplied by prayers.

When my daughter was three months old, I started an internal medicine residency. It was hard to leave my sweet daughter, but I knew that the goal was to create an easier life for her by becoming a doctor—and this is what I was made to do. While the pros and cons weighed on me, I knew that my duty was to continue on the path that led to me becoming someone concerned with the health of others to show God's love. Any hardship to my personal life was made up for by the reward of doing what was right in the long run.

This residency was six hours away from our hometown, where my husband was working. Even the language, Saraiki, was different from our area. I went to take the first history from a patient, one hour before the attending was going to make rounds.

This patient spoke the typical local language, which was completely outside of my understanding. I got extremely nervous, as I could not understand what that patient was saying! Thankfully, one of the senior residents came to help, and I was able to get a decent history.

The next morning, I was assigned one ward

consisting of twelve beds to take history for and make follow-up notes on all the patients. They were all ladies suffering for hepatic encephalopathy, a condition resulting from end stage liver disease. They were showing manifestations ranging from coma to delirium and psychosis.

I came to know that they all had hepatitis B or hepatitis C, resulting from blood transfusions or from poor hygiene, unclean needles used in medical management, etc. In those days, the donated blood was not tested prior to transfusions, and blood transfusions were very commonly used.

There were no arrangements for transplants. There, the ultimate outcome of all these patients was death, sooner or later. There was an eerie calm to seeing these women who would lose their lives. There was nothing we could do to save them, and they were resigned to their fate. The reality was that this ward was disheartening, and there wasn't a lot to offer in the way of platitudes and soothing words. We would give them medicine and strict diet plans and send them home.

Obviously, these women had families and possibly children that would grow up without mothers. Mothers without their daughters, not because of drugs like here in the West, but because the system in place had failed them. Tainted blood and needles were the problem, and there was no fixing it once the damage had occurred. I was reminded to thank God often that I had not needed a blood transfusion, and thus had escaped the dangers of the transfusion in Pakistan.

The next month I was assigned the rotation with

the nephrology ward. All the young patients in the ward were dying of kidney failure.

Dialysis was only peritoneal dialysis; no machines were available. The cost was a major issue. We learned how to do all the calculations for fluid and electrolyte balances. It was the only way it worked then, and we became quite proficient at making sure our calculations were always correct for our patients.

There was a nineteen-year-old boy being discharged, on my first day in that ward, to die at home, because he could not afford peritoneal dialysis. The unfairness of the whole ordeal struck me, and I remember praying that this young man might get better, despite the odds, to live a full and happy life. Financial barriers to treatment are a problem and reality for many families around the world. I committed in my heart to find a way to make more services available for the least of these, someday. It was outside of my realm of influence at the time.

The very next day, I admitted an eleven-year-old girl who was swollen from fluid, all over her body. Basic testing was done to help us figure out what might be happening in her body. After a urine test and a baseline blood test, she was diagnosed with nephrotic syndrome, a condition in which one loses large amounts of proteins in the urine, resulting in very low proteins in the blood. This begins causing severe swelling.

The next morning, the attending physician, after reviewing her records, discussed with the patient and her parents that there was no treatment for her condition. I still cannot forget the sadness and hopelessness that sprung up with the tears in the eyes of this eleven-year-old girl. She kept asking the attending physician if there was anything we could do. She pleaded that there must be some treatment for her disease.

My heart broke, for the second day in a row, as I watched a young life hear that they would perish. It makes the problems in first world countries look like child's play—even to first world people. Finding out that a loved one, especially a young person, will see their life end very soon, makes the smaller issues fade away to almost nothing. Who cares if you don't have the newest car when your child is terminally ill? The latest and greatest phones and fashions don't matter when a child is suffering. Not that any of those things are bad on their own. These realities don't seem existent until they are happening to you or someone you love. People touched by tragedy give to the causes that have affected them. As a doctor, all the sadness you see affects you—which is why we give of our lives to causes and people.

There were no fancy tests available in those days. A majority of diagnoses were made on the basis of detailed histories and physical examinations. Of course, this meant that underlying medical issues were missed at times, but we were good at pouring through the histories and getting to know our patients. We didn't have the technology to run through possibilities for us and make a diagnosis.

Another morning, this twenty-year-old young man was brought from a village. It was traditional for the village people to bring the sick on a portable cot, lifting him on their shoulders. The entirety of close and extended family members followed him on foot. He was in respiratory failure and was unable to swallow. Our assistant professor was making rounds that morning; he started taking a history and figured out by asking him to count from one to hundred.

As he started counting, his volume kept on going lower and lower. The professor gave him the diagnosis of Myasthenia Gravis, which is a condition where the connection between the nerves and the muscles loses function. The neurotransmitters aren't working in this area. MG (Myasthenia Gravis) is an autoimmune disease. The condition is caused by a breakdown in communication between the nerves and muscles. The muscles under involuntary and voluntary control no longer work the way they should which causes weakness and rapid fatigue.

He was given medication for the condition, as a test dose. He suddenly sat up, improved, and went home in a few days. The whole hospital was full of flowers and sweets donated by the family, which was a customary way of showing appreciation for saving a life.

We were trained to diagnose valvular heart disease by just history and physical examination. We didn't have access to echocardiograph or any other machinery.

As compared to practice of medicine, here in United States of America, less time is spent on examination, more time is expended on testing and documenting. We would perform all different maneuvers, turn the patient to left lateral position or have them lean forward to diagnose what valve was tight or leaking. We were taught to keep having the patient change positions until we could determine, with accuracy, what was going on in them.

This is lost in many practices today, because doctors must see so many patients each day to bill insurances, pay for buildings, afford staff costs, and various other costs like utilities. While doctors make a good living in the United States, there are a lot of expenses that come with the territory.

Doctors, even though they want to be humane and sensitive, are forced to become technical, using numbers and paperwork more than taking a detailed history and performing a good thorough physical examination. Just recently, an old friend of ours was visiting and he mentioned his story: He's in his 70's, an orthopedic surgeon, and had abdominal pain, nausea, and vomiting. He went to the ER, but not one doctor examined his abdomen. No one looked at his scan results in detail, a scan that was ordered without an examination. He was sent home only to be brought back to the ER a mere four days later with more symptoms. Again, many consultants came, but no one checked his abdomen. The third time he went to the ER, an Indian doctor came and found his abdomen to be tender in the right side, so he ordered an ultrasound. Our friend was diagnosed with gallbladder disease and in the operating room it was realized that his gallbladder was gangrenous. Had the Indian doctor not done a physical examination, it is possible our friend would be dead.

Modern medicine is becoming technical and mechanical, or electronic, but not humane. There is no touch, no feelings. Time is money. Insurance companies will not pay for your time if you sit with a patient to hold their hands and listen to their heart, their stories and complaints that may guide you to the vital clue which helps diagnose the disease without any tests.

The other day a RN friend of mine called me in distress, thinking that she might have a brain tumor. Just by taking her history and performing her examination I was led to the diagnosis of benign positional vertigo, a condition causing loss of balance due to fluid imbalances in the inner ear.

My goal as a physician is to keep a sense of humanity in my work. My patients are human beings created by and loved by Almighty God, and they deserve to be treated as precious. I still pray over every patient, and have no problem sharing that with them.

Chapter Eight

When New Life Meets Complications

Saving one life is equivalent to saving all of mankind. That's how important one life is.

After my internal medicine internship, I started an obstetrics and gynecology internship. This was a very different experience, and it was in the shadow and fear of my experience with the stillborn. It is understood that there is death in the medical field, that there are situations entirely outside of our control, yet that doesn't make them any easier. This internship may very well have been what spurred me to work with the elderly, facing death often, but understanding that end of life at a ripe old age is somehow easier to deal with than youngsters dying.

In order to start a practice in Pakistan, it was suggested to do internships in internal medicine and obstetrics and gynecology. Even though anyone could technically start a practice, even without any traditional training, fresh out of medical school. Those of us who wanted to do well by our patients chose to optimize our schooling with the additional internships. I knew that the extra practice would help me to be more effective. I wanted to save as many lives as I could, so I signed on to work extra hard.

Duty hours in gynecology were extremely long,

extending to fifty-six hours in one stretch. It was very difficult to stay in the labor ward for fifty-six hours without seeing my daughter. There were moments I questioned whether I had made a good decision with the extra workload.

There were times, when there was less to do, that I daydreamed about my sweet Sehar who was waiting for me at home. I would imagine her bubbly smile and giggle, and by the time a patient had presented with a complication, I would be ready to do everything I could to make motherhood a reality for the woman in labor.

As soon as a patient came to the labor ward, her husband is given a long list of medicine to buy. It was a standard list of supplies and medications. The husband was also expected to arrange a unit or two for blood transfusion. Sometimes that blood was used and sometimes it was not, but that blood was not tested for hepatitis or HIV at that time. These were not even known diseases yet.

Looking back, that is very frightening, especially after my internal medicine internship, watching young people lose their lives to diseases we didn't have a name for or understand. How very sad when medications in any country lag behind first world countries! It ties the hands of caring doctors who want to see their patients thrive, or at least survive.

There is very little prenatal care available in the villages in Pakistan. Most of the deliveries are handled by midwives in villages and suburbs. Those who come to hospitals come with dead babies with shoulders and hands hanging out. During a normal shift I would encounter breech babies, stuck by their heads in the birth canal. These breech babies would suffocate on their way to life, dead, almost delivered, such sad cases.

Sadly, it would become necessary to deal with twins where the second child was dead. While sometimes a woman would come in expecting one baby and leave with two or three. All patients are surprises that need quick backgrounds given, very few of them you know because of their clinical visits, so it is a race against time to obtain the proper information. Some were anemic due to poor nutrition or had undiagnosed medical problems. Every life was at risk of death because there was no concept of prenatal care or happiness at times of delivery. As a doctor, the level of care can depend on information. There might be reasons to make different decisions that vary from the normal path taken in the same situation with different circumstances. Dealing with emergencies changes the level of fight-or-flight in doctors and tends to be very stressful.

Working as an OB/GYN intern opened my eyes to the scary truth of *moving between the doors of life and death*. It always seemed to me that the old died, after long fulfilling lives, and that seemed fine. It wasn't as upsetting as pulling a dead baby from the body that had carried it for nine months. There was something incredibly heartbreaking about seeing a baby die on the day it was destined to begin life. There was never a moment that this normal occurrence at the hospital made me numb. It affected me every time I had to deal with it.

The ability to be affected, decades after I began my work as a doctor, has never gone away. I have heard doctors talk about not feeling what they felt when they started in their field. Suffering always affects me. I feel the need to fix it, to see the patient recover.

There are cases that some people might see and think that the person would be out of their misery if they just passed on, but I see it differently. They need to find peace before they pass on, so I pray that they may see a reprieve before God takes them in their sleep. Maybe there is a hidden hope in me that I will take no part in their death, that they will slip away while I am actively treating them and praying for their healing, so that I am not implicated in their death.

My duty is to help. Even making their dying process easier is helping. When someone is dying, there is no need to prolong the dying process to make them suffer more.

Chapter Nine

Migration and New Goals

When migration is for freedom and faith, more than the landscape changes.

Just after finishing this internship, I was expecting again, with my second daughter, and started working at a state job. A state job in Pakistan is where a doctor works with a township or community clinic that is run by the government.

This was a clinic in the suburbs. I would go to the clinic and luckily, there was a dispensary attached. There was a long line of patients outside daily, and I would check all of them.

There was no documentation needed. No worries about lawsuits or malpractices. It was a simpler time. People trusted their doctors in Pakistan, and we didn't have any plans to let them down. We didn't have to spend four hours writing down every word said during the visit to ensure that there was no funny business later. We didn't write every little detail of the exam when testing yielded no notable results. In Pakistan, when a person died, their family accepted that fate as the will of God. They wouldn't have dreamed of going after doctors!

Not one of the needy people that came to the clinic would have imagined trying to financially gain anything from their doctors by making an accusation. They desperately needed doctors, and we were a blessing to their lives. Without us, there was nowhere to go to get help when it was necessary. This is when I decided to leave my newly settled house to move to my hometown to serve the ladies of the community, as they had no female doctor.

There, I remember a lady who came with twins when I was working in the hospital in my hometown. She was in preterm labor: One was a normal baby boy who weighed 2 pounds, and the other baby was without complete development of his head, so the second baby was dead. This 2-pound baby was a challenge. There were no incubators; the baby was kept wrapped in cotton and under lamps to give him heat. He was fed with syringes. After about one month, thanks to the day and night care of the nurses (and prayers), this baby was safe for discharge home.

Moments like these were bittersweet. Of course, there was a lingering sadness surrounding the loss of one twin, but there was rejoicing and excitement over the twin that was thriving and going home. It is in these moments that you see why being a doctor is necessary and worthwhile. I would have done what was necessary to save the other twin, if anything could have been done. The living twin made all the efforts we put into his care worthwhile.

Two years were almost over for my community volunteer work, and I decided to move back home with my husband. There were more new doctors working in the department, so I was able to pull back to start the next adventure. It became the focus: Our interview for our Green Card to the USA.

****

When we landed in the United States, I was five months pregnant with my third child. I remember going to the hospital, as a patient, was very hard on me. I wanted to work and practice as a physician but coming from Pakistan presented more work to redeem the credentials I had spent so many years earning overseas. It was a new beginning that seemed redundant, yet I had to jump through the hoops to regain my ability to practice medicine.

I started preparing for my boards while I was pregnant, just a week or so after arriving to the United States. My two little daughters, two and four, were going through the psychological stress of being in a new country with new family members who they were not very connected to. Transitioning in a new land, with children, is far more difficult than if it had just been my husband and myself. It is a delicate thing to try to build relationships between family and long-lost loved ones.

After my son was born, I took my boards and passed and then took USMLE Step II (United States Medical License Examination) as well. There are four steps. Written exams, oral exams, examiners testing you with patients, then residencies follow. This was the most stressful time of my life: studying, taking care of three children, keeping up with the whole household without any help as compared to Pakistan, where I had a lot of help. I used to cry and pray aloud, when I was alone in the house and traveling back and forth on my way to examinations. When my husband would be driving, I would be wondering What does he think of me? I must seem crazy.

There is an incident that took place when I was taking my Step II that has stuck with me. I was extremely thirsty and regretted that I did not have anything to drink with me, not even a mint or candy to help my dry throat. I wished I had brought some candies with me and sat thinking about the unfortunate event of being stuck in this state of my dry throat due to stress and anxiety, with no respite.

After a few minutes of thinking about my annoyance that I had forgotten to think ahead to such a small issue, the old man who was in the examination hall supervising, brought a handful of candies for me and said, "You were the one asking for candies, right?"

I looked at him in surprise and happily accepted the gift from God. No one around had called for him to ask for anything. Later, I shared those candies with my husband and my children. This is not a common practice in the examination halls, to offer candies to the people taking the test. My gratitude to God, for granting me the ability to wet my mouth, was proof that He cared, even about things that may seem insignificant to the observer. Not one time had I opened my mouth to ask for candies, yet they were brought to me as if I had made a special request for them. I marveled over this miracle for a time. It was a blessing!

There is a story from when I was studying to pass the exam that is golden. Studying is so important, because to get into any residencies, you must score well on the exams. Sarah was at home, and I observed her picking her nose with something in her hand. She kept messing in her nose, so I finally asked, "What happened?"

She just kept pointing up toward her nostril. She had a habit of sticking various things in her nose— the edge of the blanket, toys, a tissue, so I wasn't sure what she was getting at by pointing to her nose, at first. My puzzled expression must have looked amusing to her, because when I reached for her, she grinned. Sure enough, there was a plastic button wedged in the middle of her nose, horizontally. That nostril was not taking in a lot of oxygen, and I didn't have forceps to pull the button out.

At this time, we didn't have health insurance, so I knew that this could be an expensive accident, but it was more concerning was that the button could go into an airway. My older sister happened to be over. She convinced me to take her to the emergency room, that she would drive.

My father came over with a plate of black pepper, "Let her sneeze it out! She will be fine."
"That won't work, abba jaan! We have to get this button out." I was sure that it wouldn't work, and worry kept me from taking the time to just try it.

So, we got to the emergency room with Sarah, and the doctor was blindly using forceps on her; she was not even three-years-old yet. Sarah was not having it, so after a while, one of the nurses suggested using pepper. My eyes narrowed at the suggestion that I had dismissed earlier coming from my father, and they got her to sneeze. The button didn't come out with the sneeze.

They sent us to the ear, nose, and throat specialist

next door, and he was able to easily get the button out of Sarah's nose. It's possible the sneeze made the button more accessible. Again, if the doctors in the ER had looked in her nose after sneezing, we could have saved the expense of the ENT consultation.

We got stuck with the emergency room bill, and the ear, nose, and throat doctor's bill. When I reflect on that moment, I realize that if I had just listened to my father, who had more experience in life, I would have used pepper at home and not gotten stuck with those bills. I knew my father gave sound advice, and I was reminded that I should always just listen to him. My sister and I both thought we knew better than him, with all our training, and he was right.

When I got the results of my Step II, the time to apply for match had passed. There is a matching process for residency, and the process to apply had passed by the time I took and passed the test. For the whole country, you had to apply in September. The matches were finished by January or February. When applying, the applicant would write their priorities, after interviews, to ensure that the goals were in line with the residency. At the time, people could get more than one match, but they could only accept one match (things may have changed by now).

The exact way it worked was the person looking for a residency would number their preferences for the residency. If the residency program also chose the applicant, it was a preferred match. The residency program and applicant had to choose each other, which is why it is called a match. If someone matched with more than one of their choices, the remaining choices that chose the applicant would have open seats to fill, which is called the post-match. The leftover spots are compiled into a book of available post-match opportunities.

Friends advised me to obtain a post-match book so I could apply for a residency. I started calling every morning to different programs to see if they had any openings for a residency program. I would call as early as it was acceptable to call. I remember I had full trust in God that I would get into a program, even though the chances of matching post-match are remote.

Somehow, the peace I found also motivated me. God had helped me all this time—from being able to afford medical school in Pakistan until now; I had no reason to believe that his blessings would stop now that I was starting a new life in the United States.

I kept on declaring, in front of everyone, that I know that God Almighty would get me into a residency program. One morning, while I was still asleep, I saw in my dream that there was number on the post-match book, on the top of a page, and knew I should call that number. I waited anxiously for nine a.m. to roll around and called that number. I asked if they had any first-year resident positions open, hopeful for good news on the line. I was expectant because of the dream.

The office secretary responded that they had just opened one position this morning, "Please fax your resume with a cover letter."

"Thank you, I will do that right away," I responded, and the same day I was called for an interview.

Imagine my delight when I was accepted in

the program. When I went to the same office after the interview and accepted and signed the contract for my position, I realized the cover letter I had faxed was for a pediatric residency position (as I was applying for all sorts of different positions, just to enter any residency, although internal medicine is what I always wanted to do), and this was an internal medicine residency position. I was horrified by my mistake, but no one even mentioned it to me.

I have a firm belief that this position was merely a blessing from God, as I trusted him and openly declared that God would get me into a residency program. He did better than I had declared though, because it was in exactly the field I wanted to be working in. It could have just as easily worked out that I had gotten a different residency, and I would have been happy with that, declaring it a success and blessing.

But here I was going into an internal medicine residency, just like I had prayed I would get. I gave thanks and praise for His kindness and goodness to me, in all the ways He showed it. A grateful heart is something that can't be taken away, and it seems the more I pray, and the more I honor God, the more things fit into place.

As I was the last one to join the program, I had no other option than taking one-month vacation in the second month, after completing the first month of ER (Emergency Room) rotation.

I was accepted in the program on June 27 and the same day I was supposed to go for orientation. Everything was changing rapidly, and I had to drive ninety minutes away from home to go to the emergency room, to ensure I was there at eleven a.m. Then I was off at eleven p.m., facing another ninety-minute drive. There were many Spanish speaking patients in the ER. I picked up basic words and tried to manage the best I could with the patients.

The first time I was assigned to examine a young man who was drunk and restrained; he was incontinent, soaked in sweat and urine. He was unresponsive and smelled bad, this was the first time in my life I ever smelled alcohol. In Pakistan, I never saw an alcoholic patient, all through my residency. I was very concerned to see a young man soaked in his urine, unresponsive, and tied up with restraints. All my original training hadn't prepared me for the ugly reality of self-medicating with alcohol.

When I came home after my first day in the ER, I reached home at midnight and early in the morning my three children were all over me in my bed, one on each side, with my son on my belly. They had missed me, as this was the first time in many years that they had to have dinner without me. It was a bittersweet moment, where I knew that I was pursuing my medical career in the United States, which was a duty in my life, yet, I missed the blessings God had given me while I was at the hospital working. I prayed over them and enjoyed every moment of their affections.

These changes seemed very rapid. I had been staying with the kids and studying ever since I came to the United States. I rarely drove on highways, and now I was spending three hours each day on them.

One day, I was driving on the NJ turnpike, suddenly it started raining cats and dogs. I couldn't see anything on the road, cars were stopping on the side of the road due to zero visibility. This was stressful and with me not being used to driving ninety minutes one way, I raised my hands up and let my husband know that I will not be able to drive that much every day, "That means you have to find a house near the hospital for us. That means we're moving." Qamar started looking to help my nerves on the highway that didn't have turns, or turnarounds.

I started residency on June 27, and on July Fourth we moved. My husband rented a house with two bedrooms in the area. It wasn't ideal; the neighbors were noisy. There was an abusive boyfriend downstairs. Not only had our kids never been exposed to such nonsense, we were now living in the middle of it. Our prayers ramped up. We knew we weren't staying here, but we also knew that we weren't willing to go into debt to be in a home. We were diligently saving and preparing for the time that we would have a place without this noise.

I did not know what the address was of our new abode and was coming out of the ER at around ten p.m. My attending knew that we had moved, and my husband called me to tell me that he would be outside such and such exit waiting for me, since I did not know where to go.

I was so nervous to talk to a family member during work hours that I hung up quickly. This was in the time before GPS, cellphones, and text messages. So, I was on the road without knowing where my new home was located. There was no phone at the new house, and I didn't know my address.

Qamar had shown me the house late at night in

the dark, when he was driving, and I had just noted the names of a few streets. So, here I was, on Garden State Parkway, trying to find my way, but going around and around in circles. Every time I made a new circle, throwing a token (thirty-five cents) into the tollbooth, feeling more and more lost with every pass. I was extremely nervous and distressed, praying fervently for guidance from God. The helplessness was starting to set in: Do I head back to the hospital, where at least I know where I am? At any rate, if I got there, I would know where I was.

Finally, I just came out on one exit that looked the most familiar. Coming off the exit, I did not know if I should make a right or left. I just decided to make a right, went for a few blocks. At this point, it was about one in the morning. Then, I told myself this doesn't seem right, made a U-turn and came to the other side.

On my way back, I saw my dear husband standing with a policeman. I couldn't be more thankful to Allah, how He had guided me to the spot where Qamar was waiting! If I had not taken the right turn, it would have been hard for me to locate him. Relief flooded me as I pulled in next to them. He sweetly admitted that he was extremely nervous and that he called the police. The police had told him that it's July Fourth tonight, she might be at a party somewhere! My husband told him, "My wife is not like that."

The policeman responded, "All men say that." Qamar knew better though. Of course, I would not choose a party over my husband and my children.

Finally, we made it home. That was the first time I had ever been so lost. It is a scary feeling to not know where you are going and to have no indication of which direction to head. I suppose that sometimes life can feel like that to some people, and I pray that if one thing I say can help anyone—patient, doctor, family member, or friend—find their way, that through my work and my writing someone may find peace.

There were all different patient populations at the new hospital: language issues with Spanish speaking patients was the most common barrier. I quickly learned many Spanish words along with all the new regulations and procedures for the hospital. I remember we used to handwrite all notes, no dictations. It seemed that the paperwork portion of my shifts took longer and longer than the care I was able to provide. Fifteen minutes in a room with a patient could turn into forty-five minutes to an hour of writing.

For ER rotation I was on my feet all twelve hours, with maybe half an hour to sit, for a break. I made sure that I offered my prayers in the middle of crisis, during codes, for sick patients, whether I was sitting or standing, without letting anyone know.

It can never be said enough: my prayer over my patients has done things I cannot. God is faithful and kind, and He hears our prayers. I can't prove a positive. For instance, I cannot tell you how many times a patient may have had complications, but prayer stalled the difficulties. I can tell you of the times that the outlook was grim and something supernatural happened.

We will never know how many times God has intervened on our behalf, until He tells us someday. I sometimes think that if I had told them I need the time or place to offer my prayers, my attending would have accommodated me, but not having a set place and time didn't stop me from praying.

The second month, I was forced to take a vacation because I had joined the group last and every other month was already taken. So, we used this month to look for a house outside of the neighborhood we were currently in. Looking for a house in North Jersey area was a big hassle. We would drive all day, looking at houses in very shabby areas, houses that offered no parking, no driveways, and were far beyond our limited budget.

After searching for a few months, we found a space on the third floor of an apartment building, with no elevators. This wasn't ideal, but desperation to leave the current house outweighed taking several more months of looking that may have yielded similar results, just months down the road.

In one month rotation, I was shocked by the numbers of certain illnesses that showed up simultaneously. I saw multiple ailing patients, actually very ill, who were admitted to ICU with CHF, cirrhosis of the liver, and many acutely sick people brought in to the hospital in very critical condition. Maybe even more shocking was as soon as they woke up, they would sign against medical advice and go back home to stop taking their meds and quit watching their diet, back to drinking, taking drugs, etc. Ultimately, they would end up coming back the next week in the same situation. I wondered and still think about how many resources are used on these people to make them feel better for just a few days to remain in the same condition due to poor lifestyle choices.

Why do we do that? Are we helping humanity, or we are covering our back to avoid a lawsuit? There must be a choice made, by the patient, and it can't be made for them to enter recovery or wellness. For instance, if an alcoholic or drug addict will not take the steps to be well, no doctor on this planet can force them to stop drinking or doing drugs. If we tell someone with Diabetes II that they can improve or repair their condition with proper diet and exercise, if they continue to choose not to eat right and exercise regularly, that is not the fault of the doctor.

It is common that doctors hit brick walls with stubborn patients. We are here to help, yet there are some people who do not want to be helped. We hear the family's plea for their loved ones, yet we are powerless without cooperation.

The most striking difference I noticed in the practice here was documentation, documentation, and after that, some more documentation. If you document something and don't do it, it counts like you did it, but if you did it and spent hours in serving a sick patient, but did not document, you did nothing. If things go wrong, then you are not able to stand against any claims. That is why we spend so much time documenting, when our heart is with helping the patients. This was the first lesson I was given by a senior resident. They were adamant that I fully understand how medicine in the United States works, so that I wouldn't run into any complications.

One more thing that I saw was the review of old records. We had to go to medical records department at any time, during the night or day, to get big piles of charts. The chore began by opening page after page, trying to read the scribbles of all the numerous doctors' old notes. It seemed to consume hours, taking the time to turn the numerous pages, to make out a history of these charts for an unresponsive patient with no family members. Doctors are notorious for horrible handwriting, so imagine the task that really was at hand, just to try to do right by the patient. It is a blessing to have electronic records available now, where I can go through an entire chart in much less time.

The first year of residency was the most stressful time, for me, and most likely, for many others. All first-year residents were treated like the youngest person who runs around in a car garage, but when it comes to putting pressure, presenting in morning report, it was all put on the shoulders of the first year. After running around like a puppet all night, in the morning you are presenting in front of all those doctors, residents, and attendings who slept well last night. They all attack you with questions. All the admissions from the previous night were presented to the program director and she could pick any of the cases to have you elaborate on. First Year Resident stands on the podium to present the case and presents the differential diagnosis. Others, who are sitting in the audience, ask you different questions to try to put your brain through their scrutiny. It felt like you were being punished for staying up all night on your feet. To add insult to injury, I was not fresh out of medical school with no experience. I had been a practicing doctor in Pakistan before coming here.

Once you present one case, you will never forget that for the rest of your life. It has its benefits.

I remember one interesting case that we presented, with green sclera and yellow discoloration of the skin. This was an interesting case of a patient with osteogenesis imperfecta. In this case, the collagen does not form completely and results in bluish sclera. This patient had some kind of hepatitis and jaundice that resulted in green sclera (the white part of the eye).

Some of the patients were so sick that they were repeatedly admitted in the hospital, to the point that you just memorized their history, you knew it by heart.

Patients were coming in with heart attacks, going into shock and severe distress, going on the ventilator and requiring CPR. There were patients with HIV (in those days, HIV treatments were not as good as they are now), so we would see many cases with opportunistic infections. This could become an unfortunate cycle for the patients, because their immune systems were so compromised that while having a virus, there would be other breakout illnesses. Sometimes, they couldn't recover from the barrage of bacteria and viruses in their system, and they would lose their lives. You could just look at a patient and tell that they had pneumonia due to HIV, it had its own distinct characteristics.

One more interesting case I remember was white clot syndrome. In heparin-induced thrombocytopenia with thrombosis, or "White-clot syndrome," patients have paradoxic thromboembolic events while receiving heparin. These events are of acute onset and of major consequence, often resulting in limb loss or death.

Ray was admitted with a heart attack, and he developed a condition called HIT. Within the week, he developed a stroke due to white clot syndrome. HIT can happen when a patient has a stroke or a heart attack. They are immediately put on a blood thinner, like heparin, intravenously. After a few days, the patient is put on Warfarin (Coumadin), or one of the newer anticoagulant drugs, to prevent coagulation (clotting) of the blood. Heparin can cause a reaction in some patients, where antibodies form against the platelets.

There are three types of cells in the blood—the white blood cells, red blood cells, and platelets. When the platelets rapidly decrease, some people develop what is called white clot syndrome, which causes strokes and deep vein thrombosis, from blood clots. So, when treating certain things, other issues can be caused, which is why doctors monitor progress throughout treatment. Follow-up appointments are incredibly important, so doctors can catch things like this.

After the first year of residency, I decided to move to another program that was still in NJ, but closer to my house, but here, the second year was given the most responsibility while first years were treated like babies and protected by the program director. So, that means all the stress of presenting in the morning report was on the second year, so I got stuck doing it again. Here, the first-year residents did not have to stand on the podium. Even though I felt very unhappy, with no relief, but it was good for my learning process. It is no secret that I adhere to the mantra that when you do more work, you learn more.

Third year was better than the other two years.

Patients stick with doctors. We remember their cases and sympathize with what they went through, which is why I am so clear on these case studies I am sharing. Any doctor that decides to share some memories is only sharing a small percentage of what they have seen in their careers. This is the case with me as well, if I had written my diary every night, this could have been more detailed.

Another sad case was a gentleman who was running a successful business and had the habit of drinking heavily on a regular basis. His children had all gone away to start their own lives and weren't involved in the family business. He hired an office person to help in the daily duties, but she began controlling every aspect of his business while he lived in a cabin far away, drinking.

She took over the business completely, and he ended up in an assisted living facility. He was deemed incapable of running his business, due to being confused by the dementia caused by alcoholism. I went to check on him, and he made complete sense, telling me how he was being taken advantage of. His daughter had no clue that her father was being taken for all he had, due to her abandonment of him. This all happened because of alcohol and not staying connected with family. With his permission, I called his daughter, and I don't know what happened after I made the call. Hopefully, things were sorted out, but it is hard to tell.

As I mentioned before, alcohol wasn't something I saw until America, and I had no clue what damage it did, beyond the body, until some of my patients shared their stories with me. This gentleman taught me that being a doctor goes beyond just medicine; the responsibilities must encompass the personal wholeness of the patient. That began to mean getting patients help beyond myself. I saw cases of abuse, which switched my role from doctor to mandatory reporter. Sadly, not everyone wants the help that is available. That was a hard lesson to learn.

I saw a patient who was in her eighties. She took care of her husband until he died, and she was still a very beautiful woman. She had been a model in her younger years, and she was preoccupied with her body and staying in shape. She dressed well, did her make-up daily, and looked younger than she was. She found this guy, who she thought was perfect.

He tried to move in with her in a month. He cooked for her, spoiled her, and I am sure it was exciting after losing her husband, especially at her age. She married him quicker than anyone expected. Her children were completely against it! He was younger than her. Maybe they were concerned he was using her for her money. He was controlling.

Her visits with me changed. She would come see me and say that she had made a mistake. Apparently, Mr. Charming had become controlling and abusive. She confessed that at night, he held her so tight she felt suffocated.

I would direct her to where she could go—shelters and other places that would help. I would remind her that I couldn't make the decision for her. I called the abuse in, and authorities talked to her, but she wouldn't tell them all the things she had shared with me.

Domestic violence, or abuse originating in the home, is a very dangerous threat to the well-being and safety of females and males. Unfortunately, a lot of people don't seek the help they need due to fearing the loss of the relationship that they are comfortable in, which would lead to unknown circumstances for some time after leaving the damaging circumstances. Sometimes people don't seek help because of threats that have been made against them, other family members, property, or something else dear to the abused person's heart. There are many variables and reasons why abused people don't seek help, but it can lead to serious injuries and death.

As a medical doctor, I am a mandatory reporter, when I am aware of abuse. Many times, patients that are living in fear don't share what really happens to them. Please, if you are reading this and are dealing with abuse at home, let a medical professional help you (if you don't have a way to get help from the police). We can get you in touch with local groups that can help with living arrangements, food, mental wellness groups, as well as many more services.

This is the sad thing about helping people— they must want help. They must be active participants in their treatment plans and life for any help to work. Unfortunately, a lot of people will not do the work required to change their lives. I had to learn to accept this while still reporting and still directing patients to get help.

After three years, I took my boards and passed it, which was a relief. It also meant that I had to find a place to work.

Chapter Ten

Jewish Elderly Care

End of life care is an opportunity to show love and that their lives mattered.

During my nine years of practice at the Jewish nursing home, I became very comfortable in discussing end of life issues with the residents or their loved ones, if residents were not capable of making their decisions. Around that time, the concept of Palliative Care was just being considered: This was the new concept of keeping residents comfortable in the facility, rather than transporting them to the ER at the last moments of their life.

Palliative care. Hospice care. These concepts, that we are now comfortable with, were cutting edge and hotly debated when they first emerged in the medical field. They were not an accepted standard overnight.

Palliative care is living in comfort, not being put through unnecessary testing, poking, and probing. In Palliative Care, there is only the ability of doing those tests or procedures that will improve the outcome, not measures to prolong discomfort and pain. Treating a person as a whole, not as body parts, and considering family support in the care plan should be absolute and forefront when a doctor is assessing a patient.

Hospice Care, in contrast, is the care of one who is dying. There are signs doctors can see beforehand that predict that the patient may not be alive in six months.

I launched the first Palliative Care Program in the facility and started making rounds to ensure symptoms, and especially pain control, were being managed properly. I got so involved in this that the administration at that time recommended me to take Palliative Care and Hospice boards.

So, I took my Palliative Care and Hospice boards and passed. This was at the time that pain was called the fifth vital sign, and the use of narcotics was liberal.

There were many challenges in dealing with these patients and their family members! I remember there was a patient who belonged to an Orthodox Jewish sect. She had severe dementia, and she was having difficulty with swallowing as well as repeated pneumonia, due to food going in the lungs instead of down her food pipe.

Sadly, due to her wishes, her family wanted her to have everything done, so she had a feeding tube placed, but as shown in studies, feeding tubes do not prevent pneumonia. She required repeated hospitalizations. Due to being in the bed all the time, she developed pressure areas, which are incredibly painful. I had multiple discussions with her family to consider Hospice or Palliative Care. Her family insisted on repeated hospitalizations.

It was difficult to see her in pain. As her physician, I wanted to alleviate her suffering by allowing her to have pain medicine. We tried to optimize her pain control, but due to side effects, the optimum dose was not possible. This was also a time when nurses felt uncomfortable with dispensing liberal pain meds, due to the fear of respiratory depression caused by morphine. She had multiple hospital admissions. With each admission, when she came back, she was worse than when she left. It was common to see declines in health with every hospital visit.

The end of life can be a very painful process. That was one of the reasons that Palliative Care came into existence—to make the end of life process easier. Doctors can lack the courage to tell desperate families and patients not to treat the diseases, at a certain stage of dying you only treat symptoms like pain and shortness of breath. Doctors have an inner drive to save lives, so it is hard for us to not do something to save the life in front of us—even when the patient's wishes might be to act out their end of life plan.

All these nice ladies at the nursing home were treated with dignity and respect. They were dressed up in nice outfits with matching jewelry. They had their hair done and their clothes pressed. There wasn't an amenity withheld.

I fondly remember some elderly women who insisted on wearing heels, no matter how unsteady they were, even with the risk of falls they persisted in click-clacking down the halls. I always laughed, thinking I might be that elderly lady in the future, high heels and all!!

This world seems to create new narratives for history, and it came to my attention, during the writing of this book, that there are theories that the Holocaust never happened. As a doctor who has worked with Holocaust survivors, I was shocked that such rumors even existed.

I know the Holocaust happened. I have seen the absolute horror written in the lives of these patients. Their ability to forgive and thrive is astonishing.

Alzheimer's is a weird thing. It works in three stages. In mild (early) Alzheimer's, the patient knows what's happening, but they are starting to not respond like they once did. They forget and repeat questions. They become restless and anxious due to fear of losing control. In moderate (middle) stage Alzheimer's, they start thinking and going back to their earlier formative years, and they talk about what happened at those times in their lives. These memories are not made up, their brains couldn't handle this. What they are saying is real, and they were all saying the same things. Severe (late) stage Alzheimer's is when there aren't as many behaviors, due to the progression of the disease.

Alzheimer's affects every patient differently, so the timing and severity of dementia symptoms varies as each person progresses through the disease. The mild and moderate stages of Alzheimer's are difficult due to increased agitation because the patient us aware that they are losing control of their bodies and minds. Severe stages of dementia are difficult in patients due to their functional decline.

This was a chapter of my life where I spent nine years. The reason was that the work schedule was easy, and on-call was only a phone call. I did not have to go in. I was just expected to answer the nurses and instruct them on what was best to do in the situation that they were calling about. I quite enjoyed the freedom that this allowed me with my family.

Ultimately, as my employers kept on taking advantage of me, which they had been doing since I started working with them, I had to figure something else out for my career. They gave me the minimum salary and did not offer me the partnership that was promised.

As I worked to figure out what the next step of the journey was, something horrible happened. Something no one was prepared for in the entire United States.

Chapter Eleven

9/11

If your religious beliefs tell you to kill the inno-cent, you are not part of a faith anyone in their right mind wants to believe in.

Nothing can prepare you for the tragedy that Americans lived through on September 11, 2001. When hearing about the events and how they unraveled, it seemed that time stood still, and every piece of me wondered what type of nightmare this was. It didn't seem real.

When the initial reports started naming the men responsible for the attacks, and their religious affiliation, fear set in. Believe me, this topic fits this book, and begs to be addressed.

During the time of 9/11, it was very hard to deal with the embarrassment, as the name of Islam was used, and a completely wrong picture of Islam was portrayed in the media, due to the actions of the wrong people.

There were times fear reigned, as we saw the anger that was being verbalized against our faith. Sadly, we understood the hatred being spewed, because this was a horrible thing that had happened. Many families lost husbands and wives, fathers and mothers, sons and daughters, children. The attacks spanned four planes and three locations, of course the outcry would be massive.

This tragedy also gave me opportunities to share

my true faith and the true teachings of my faith with my colleagues and friends, as they asked multiple questions. I was happy to answer and remove the misconceptions about Islam that were being portrayed by the media.

The most dangerous monster is one you don't understand. Islam was being made into a monster, and without clear understanding, many Americans were left dealing with emotions that are understandable, but not fair.

People who knew me had seen me as a person and knew that my ideas and beliefs were contradictory to the actions of extremists. Due to all the changes in the world that resulted after 9/11, my husband was asked to resign from his job, as the company was "down-sizing." Suddenly, there were new decisions to be made for the well-being of our family.

We were close to New York, and the pleas for missing family members was enough to break your heart every time you saw one. Families clung to hope that their family member was in a hospital or in hiding. Every time I saw a family searching for someone, I would pray—that they would find them and for peace if they did not.

News stations ran updates on the searching, for weeks, and sadly, the collapse of the Twin Towers took more lives than were recovered from the wreckage. We saw the weary heroes—police, firemen and women, rescue workers, EMTS, rescue dogs, volunteers, clergy— search until they couldn't move another step. We prayed for all of them too. The helplessness of the situation drove us to pray and pray until we would fall asleep, waking to begin our prayers again.

9/11 changed the landscape—at Ground Zero, but also for Muslims in the country. My husband and I felt horrible about fellow Americans dying. I cannot imagine what my kids were going through while dealing with it in school, where kids are very vocal about what they hear and feel. We were made to feel guilty about our faith. This attack had disfigured the name of Islam. Our sect was having the worst days of our lives—we were persecuted by Muslims, and now we were being persecuted by non-Muslims for being Muslim.

There was a woman who worked at my office, Patricia, as a CNA (Certified Nurse's Aide). She was in her late 50's and had been at the facility for over 20 years. Her experience and compassion made her stick out above the rest, so she was the one running the office. I trusted Patricia and appreciated her caring, conscientious, and emotional approach to my patients, which is why she was the first point of contact with them. She was an extension of me.

Her brother was a firefighter that responded to the 9/11 attack. He was actively working to save lives at Ground Zero, immediately following the planes hitting the buildings. He was able to bring people out of the World Trade Center that he was in, and after leading and carrying a group to safety, he went back in to save more lives. That's when the building came down, while he was racing up the stairs to find others in need.

When Patty found out, her grief was shared at the office. Her pain affected us all, and I was close to her, so my heart broke. I took meals to her and tried to comfort her every chance I got. She still sends me cards on my birthday and calls from time to time. May the memory of her brother be a blessing, for the selflessness he exhibited as he gave up his life for his fellow man and woman on that fateful day.

After a few years of my husband trying to find the right job, my husband and I decided to move to another state in the pursuit of starting my own practice. It was time to make changes, and I wanted to be my own boss. The state we were in was congested with practices. No more broken promises from employers. I was going to take the chance to make my own practice, be in charge of my policies, and do things my way. Tragedy has a way of changing priorities.

My children got very upset with the idea of moving and advised me not to look further south than Pennsylvania. We were accustomed to living on the East Coast, and with the way life was there. Things had to change though. There was a fire burning inside of me, lit by the lunacy of the attack, and I wanted to help more people than my rotation at the nursing home would allow.

I pledged to take on as many cases as I could, and not be deterred by the difficulty of the patient's needs. There is a lot to say about elder care, but it is important to note, that even with my credentials and abilities, I was not immune to the fallout of a national crisis. I was heartbroken and spurred to do more for my fellow countrymen and women, like every other American. Immigrants have a unique place in society here. War is awful when we consider how many innocent people—children and animals—get killed. I always wonder about the people giving orders for war, how they sleep at night with their hands, their whole bodies, drenched with the blood of innocent people.

We are from a place we call home, but when we make this our home, there are invisible bonds that we feel. Some immigrants come at very young ages, spend their entire lives here, but are still considered an immigrant. We are all Americans, and even though I am from another country, this attack hurt the American in me. I love this country and have built a life here—I do not see myself as Pakistani, but as American first. This is part of my faith—to love the country I live in.

I appreciate all the people who loved me after the attacks, and I understand the people who may have been crass at the time. It is unfortunate that such an atrocity ever happened, and my family and I bear the scars, as well. We will never forget the victims of the attack.

Chapter Twelve

Being My Own Boss

Striking out to do something new is the only way you will know if something new will work. It is scary, but it's worth it.

After 9/11, my husband was still working with a prestigious communications company. They started to lay employees off, cutting the number of workers they had down as the economy panicked from the attack. He was let go, with a severance package. I was still working, but I felt strongly that it was time for a change. Sadly, we felt that there was discrimination in the layoff of Qamar—we didn't speak about it, but we were darker and had Muslim names.

We would always get medical journals in the mail, and one time, we saw that there was a medical practice for sale in Tennessee. The practice was priced so low we thought it might be a good idea to buy the practice.

There were perks to Tennessee that New Jersey didn't have. The cost of living was substantially lower. There were great colleges for the kids to go to someday. Our discussions confirmed that we wanted to build our own business, so we decided to fly out to see the facility.

The lady that was selling it was incredibly happy we were looking at buying it, but on the day, we were to sign the formal papers, a colleague of mine pulled me aside, "They should be paying you to start a practice.

141

People get paid to start practices here."

I didn't understand what he meant, so he encouraged us to call administrators of hospitals and tell them that I was interested in buying the practice to see if they would help financially. The administrator offered some help at that time. After prayer and no confirmation that we were making the right choice, we didn't buy the practice in Tennessee.

This began the search for opportunities across the United States. We travelled all over, and at one point, I was tired of looking. I resigned myself to the understanding that right now was not the right time. The children were telling us that they didn't want to move past Pennsylvania, which made the decision that much harder, so I wanted to give up.

Qamar and I were on a plane, coming back from another fruitless visit to see an available practice, and I asked him to get me a map of Pennsylvania. I saw this little town, Chamberlain. My eyes zeroed right on to it, focusing to see this little scribble amidst much bigger cities. Remembering the name, I had him put the map back.

The very next day, Qamar called and surprised me, "There's a lady that called, she wants to talk to you." He mentioned that it was an opportunity with another doctor, which was not part of my plans, so he requested, "Please talk to her."

"No, I'm not. I don't want to work with someone else." There was nothing in me that wanted a shared medical practice. What if the other doctor and I didn't get along?

Eventually, I did call her, and she convinced me to go into practice with her. She brought up the benefits of sharing a practice with another doctor: being able to take vacations and travel more, because there was someone else to share the load; shared expenses; she was already practicing, so things were set up. At the end of our conversation, she quipped, "Just come see, it can't hurt anything. I would really like to meet you."

Qamar and I decided to go the next day. The destination was none other than Chamberlain, Pennsylvania. Once I knew where we were headed, I also understood the providence of me requesting the state map and focusing in on Chamberlain. This was no coincidence. This was where God wanted me to go. I knew that before we got there. I was also aware that she would do as the previous doctors had done to me. This proved true and after one year, I provide her notice that I was not going to work with her anymore and started my own practice.

My involvement with my religious community was extensive, and in the blink of an eye, I was leaving the community. It was very touching and emotional for me, especially when one of the women presented the poem she had written for me. At my farewell, she asked in the poem: What would happen to the community with me leaving, since I had been president so long. That tugged at my heartstrings, but I knew that I was making the right move for our family and that there would be a new president who would take over and do well.

The hospital in Chamberlain gave me a two-year guarantee on my salary, plus moving expenses. In a dream, I had seen that wherever I moved, there would be a beautiful mosque built. Concerns about having a mosque didn't enter my mind due to that dream. It was great, because when we moved in, Qamar was voted the president of this chapter of the community, within a few months. I was happy for him. My husband had supported me during the seven years when I was president and regional president. I worked like a robot, day and night, and he was with me. He traveled different places with me. Now, I had the opportunity to support him, and I did. He drove an hour every day, after work, and came back late at nights, but I didn't mind and did what I could to alleviate any stress that I could prevent, which meant not adding to it. I knew how much work being the president of the community was. He got involved in building a mosque—another dream fulfilled.

Joining a medical practice is no walk in the park. Within one year, my fears were proven right, and I could tell that my decision to join someone in practice was not right, therefore I decided to move on to my own practice. We moved to a new area and I started a practice where no one knew me. In a way, it was exciting, but the 'what-if's' are incredible in this process. I would wonder if anyone would come to see me. This led me down the rabbit hole of thinking 'what if no one came, or not enough people fast enough. Would this endeavor sink, instead of swim?'

Failure wasn't an option. We had just uprooted our entire family—taken our children out of school and away from the familiar. People always need a doctor, and I provided that service for them. Surely, this might be easy. At least, I prayed it would be.

What a difference it was, practicing in a suburban area, rather than an urban area!

People were appreciative and caring. They were nice and polite; no difficult family members to order me around like I didn't know what I was doing. Most of my patients were understanding and respectful of my opinion. I almost didn't know how to conduct myself. I was still programmed to rebut arguments, and I wasn't getting any. It was a relief, and I would sigh a sigh of relief every time I encountered my patients and their families. Mostly, I would wonder what took me so long to take this step!

Like I said, in the beginning I was not very optimistic that I would be able to build my practice. Truthfully, I figured I would probably spend my time sitting in the office reading books, but that was not the case! My first day in the office, I had fifteen patients booked. I was astounded at the first day's numbers and thanked God for my patients and for the future patients He was entrusting me with.

Soon after, I found out that my brother-in-law had been diagnosed with cancer. My baby sister's husband had started having severe itching, out of nowhere. Benadryl, steroids, and all the anti-itch medications were failing him. Nothing was helpful. He became desperate for relief and went for testing.

The blood test was suggesting that something was seriously wrong. ERCP, which is a camera that goes from the mouth to the stomach to the pancreas with dye, showed a tumor at the pancreatic duct. I was one of the support systems for my sister. I made myself available to be on the phone with her day and night; every miniscule change in his condition was discussed.

After two and half years, my loving and kind brother-in-law, my younger sister's loving and caring husband, passed away. There are no words when someone you love passes away. It can only be felt with the heart. The thought crosses my mind that I would not have been as available if I had been working for someone else. I am so grateful to God that He moved on our hearts to ensure that I was in the position to be there for my little sister and her husband. I also wondered at and acknowledged how much support a family member needs in situations like catastrophic illness.

Within the first two years of my practice, I was offered medical directorship of three facilities. That helped with the overhead, and I again got actively involved with the care of the elderly. At this stage of my life, being on call day and night, was part of building the practice. I I would go into the ER at two a.m. when I was called, getting home at five in the morning just to open the doors of the practice by eight in the morning. When office hours ended, I would make hospital rounds, some days attending emergency calls for my patients, running from the office to the hospital then back to the office. There were nursing home patients to visit. That was how traditional internal medicine was practiced. This was my passion—to serve elderly patients. I have a heart for those who reside in facilities. Sadly, not many doctors in the area wanted to practice in these facilities.

With changes in the healthcare system, the population that used to be in nursing homes were accepted into assisted living, and personal care homes and those who belonged in hospitals were being admitted to nursing homes for subacute care. These patients had multiple medical problems and were recovering either from surgeries or after strokes, heart attacks, congestive heart failure, or other multiple acute illnesses.

Previously, they would stay in the hospital for seven to ten days and would undergo rehab during their stay. Then they would be discharged home, but now they were being discharged home in three days to continue rehab and post-acute care in these facilities. The nursing staff was not trained to take care of such unstable patients.

Family members, in this area, were more understanding, accepting, and respectful. That still didn't settle the unease in some nursing staffs. They were trained and available for easier patients with less problems. The instability of post-acute care is stressful on nurses who are used to stable patients.

Due to my passion to help the terminally ill, and due to my board certification in Hospice and Palliative Care, I also accepted a position as the medical director of a Hospice Program. This involved taking care of those patients who were terminally ill. A doctor has to predict that the life expectancy of the patient is less than six months before hospice care is an option. Nurses, social workers, health aides, chaplains, and volunteers provide regular services while doctors visit every sixty days to certify the patient to stay on hospice care.

I remember visiting a patient at his home. Robert was living alone in a three-bedroom ranch house. He had dementia and heart problems along with diabetes.

Most of his days were spent in his bedroom sleeping. Due to forgetfulness, he let the water run or maybe some of the plumbing system went bad; either way, the water overflowed in the bathroom which resulted in his bedroom wall being broken and water damaged.

One of his children, who had Power of Attorney for financial management, cashed a claim from insurance, but did not fix the damage. Maybe they figured he wouldn't know the difference, or maybe they needed the money—the whole situation saddened me.

He had the ability to be in his own home. It was a nice house. What struck me, when I was there, was a hallway outside his bedroom, that had pictures of children on each wall. I was told that he had married twice and had six children. Both his wives had passed away. But his caregiver was not any of his children.

There was an ice cream store next to the house. Robert and his wife used to walk to the ice cream place every evening and had become friends with the owner of this ice cream parlor. The owner had become the caregiver of this lonely, elderly gentleman. Ultimately, this house was taken over by the bank, and he was placed in a nursing home. Most likely, Robert rarely had visitors.

On my way back, I kept on thinking about all those children this guy had raised, spent his nights with them when they were young, helped them go through school, possibly paying for their education, maybe even walked some down the aisle or helped finance their lives in some way, and now he's being taken care of by a lady who has nothing in the way of relationship with him.

There is being alone, and then there is loneliness.

While the physical act of being alone can be daunting, loneliness is tangible. One could hope that Robert was too far gone in his mind to realize that his six children had abandoned him in his time of need. Sometimes, I wonder if that level of realization adds to the damage in the mind.

Robert still crosses my mind when I think of him curled in his bed, counting his breaths. What happens when someone isn't cared for by their family in our society? Do we always know? It is easy to assume that everyone is cared for, especially if you are from a loving and respectable home. There are countless elderly people who need to have someone who cares.

A forty-year-old man, named Sean, came to be seen. He had the habit of always having a toothpick in his mouth. One day, while he was driving, he swallowed a piece of the toothpick. He explained to us that he had pain ever since. We ordered an endoscopy to see if the toothpick was lodged inside him somewhere. The gastroenterologist said there were no findings due to pain in the abdomen, just inflammation. Their only option was to send him back to me. I ordered a colonoscopy to check, and again, we found nothing.

Sean still complained of discomfort, so I decided to have him swallow the capsule with a camera to see if we could determine anything that way. Again, we found nothing of concern, so there was nothing I could do.

Not so long after that, Sean went to the emergency room, and they found an abscess in his colon. The toothpick was inside of the abscess. After surgery to remove the wayward toothpick, Sean ended up with a colostomy bag. I was very saddened to hear the news, because we had tried to find it.

Sometimes, these bizarre cases cross the doctor's path. As a medical practitioner, I remember my clients, and I sometimes mull over the cases to ensure that if I ever saw something similar, I would use additional tools and resources to solve the problem sooner.

There are two lessons that I will spell out for you. One, be kind to everyone, because when you get in a position to need something from a neighbor, you want them to think fondly of you. Don't be superficial, just be kind. Two, if you are able, try to visit a nursing home near you. Do a craft with the people there or sit and talk. You might be the only contact with the outside world that the elderly person you spend time with has. That's a beautiful thing! You might be surprised at what their knowledge and experience could add to your life, while you give of your life to them.

Chapter Thirteen

A Doctor that Travels

When one is meant to save lives, they will go to the ends of the earth to find lives in need of saving.

My husband and I both love to travel. We try to travel at least every six months, if not every three to four months. We took trips with very young children, teenaged children, and now that the children are grown up, we travel without them.

As a doctor, when you are traveling, you see disease around you, and you want to intervene to help, but you cannot enter someone's private zone without their permission.

I remember one time we were on a cruise and there was a girl sitting next to me. She was not covered up. I could see a mole on her upper back that looked like melanoma, and of course, I wanted to say something.

I kept on questioning myself, Should I ask her if she has had it checked by biopsy, or not?

Ultimately, I gave in to my inner desire of helping to save a life, so I started talking to this lady next to me, "And by the way, did you get the skin lesion on your back checked?"

She had not, but I alerted her to the concern. We did not stay in touch, so I will never know whether the woman from the cruise followed up on the mole.

She hadn't been able to see it well, so hadn't noticed any changes in it, but was grateful for my advice.

Doctors are unable to close their doctors' eyes. We are accidentally working whether we are at family gatherings, meetings, or traveling. When we see a person, and notice that something is off, our doctor eyes start calculating shortness of breath and assessing the person in front of us. Many times, when people know we are doctors, they will walk up and start telling us their symptoms or about a medical problem they are facing. There are people that try to get us to diagnose someone we have not seen; out of concern, they will list someone they loves' symptoms for us to give an opinion on. We cannot diagnose, but we can suggest tests to ask primary physicians for.

Once we became empty nesters, and we felt a little relief from our familial responsibilities, we decided to give more to the people who are in need. Being involved in serving our community and local people in need did not feel like enough to me. In December, one of my friends invited me to join her on a medical mission trip. The mission trip was to Guatemala.

In the beginning, I felt scared and apprehensive, but with the reassurance of my husband, and other people, I became comfortable and excited with the idea of going on a medical mission.

We had fifteen students from Texas University, two doctors from the US, in addition to one pediatrician from Canada, three local (Guatemalan) doctors, and one local dentist on our team. We were told to get medical samples and some of us purchased medications. There were fifteen large duffle bags full of toys, hygiene kits, and various other things that were needed for the success of this mission.

When we landed at La Aurora airport in Guatemala City, we disclosed the bags for the mission camp. All the team members arrived at around the same time, all fifteen of us were kept at the airport for many hours due to the medications we had brought with us. The authorities had decided that they needed to investigate our credentials and travel arrangements more.

After many hours of investigations and discussions with the authorities, we were allowed to enter the country. We had left early in the morning, and we were all extremely hungry and tired at this point. This setback was minor, but at the time it was scary—what if they were going to turn us away, or worse detain us?

We were welcomed by the organization, Humanity First. We were there to be part of the Gift of Health Medical Mission. We were taken to a nice hotel and had a great dinner. Nothing looked much different than home, not yet.

The next morning, we were all ready, in scrubs, two large wagons were waiting for us to take us to the campsite. As we went through the cobblestone and old brick roads of Antigua, Guatemala, the jerky movements of the vehicle were very noticeable. Ultimately, we reached the town Alotenango.

There was a township building set up for us; blue-colored curtains were arranged to make small cubicles for the doctors. Our concern grew as we noticed the building was empty, and there were no patients. I got worried that there might not be any patients to see, after all the efforts and sacrifice we had gone through to arrive.

Next door, there was another courtyard that was full of people sitting in chairs. There was something cooking in a large vessel and snacks were available. There was a drum beating and the whole place was decorated. I thought there was a wedding going on, but upon questioning, I was told that these were all our patients, who had been waiting to be seen since seven a.m.; imagine, our presence there was an occasion.

Once the day started, one after the other, desperate patients—undernourished, weak, pale looking mothers of dozens of children who looked older than their stated age, nursing their children who were two, three, four-years-old came through to be seen.

Compassion moved through me, a tangible force to be reckoned with. I couldn't stop crying when I saw all these needy patients, tears continuously flowing down my cheeks. I felt so helpless and didn't know how to help these people who need so much. The thought I had was, Will our efforts be enough? They were not enough, for sure.

When I mentioned nutrition or milk to these ladies, they said that they don't have money to pay for the milk or meats that would be welcomed into their meager diets. Most of the people we were seeing were living on tortillas and beans. When I felt very sad and couldn't stop crying, my dear husband gave some cash donations to the poor. It was a drop in the ocean, but he did what he could to appease my frustration and sadness.

When a language barrier is present, but you

have so much compassion in your heart, nothing is an obstacle! Your love, your smile, and your compassion transfers straight from your heart to the patients' hearts.

And then, something happened that had never happened throughout my medical career. I checked one patient's blood sugar and when taking the needle out of the glucometer, it stuck deep in my finger. The first needle finger stick of my life! I was scared to death! Fear and horror of HIV, hepatitis, or something I wouldn't know went through my mind. That's what happens when you work in the medical field and there is a mishap—you run through the worst-case scenarios.

I used an alcohol pad on my finger and kept seeing my next patient, but just after that I was on the phone with my sister, who is an HIV consultant. I knew to start the prophylaxis as soon as possible. I went out of the cubicle and looked for the patient immediately.

Luckily, the patient was still sitting in the long pharmacy line, so we asked him to have labs taken. He agreed to go for additional testing, and medical problems like HIV or hepatitis continued to run through my head, so I needed to act for my own peace of mind.

He was advised to get tested, while I was taken to a hospital about two hours away. The hospital was in a bad condition. The chairs were broken, it was dismal and in unhygienic condition. There were blood stains on the walls and in the toilet; all around me were incredibly alarming things that didn't ease my mind from the concerns of contamination. I almost regretted coming to the hospital, because it seemed that I could be in danger, even here at the medical facility.

Half of the day was gone just because of that finger stick. I was given prophylactic medicine that I took for a few days. I was unhappy that my little negligence took my half day away from the people I came to help.

A huge problem here was the unequal distribution of money. The country is full of resources, but poor people remain poor while the rich people, who may only be the top five percent of the country, are extremely wealthy.

While helping these needy people, I felt that there was much more that needed to be done. Not that I was not helping in the United States, but here in Guatemala I was helping poor people who didn't have access to any medical care, and that did something for my soul.

During the medical mission, we started out in the one city, and after three days, the flow of patients had slowed down from coming to the medical camp because we had seen everyone that needed to be seen in that area. We decided to go to another town to continue seeing people in need. From one town to another there was a huge change in the socioeconomic status, and surprisingly, there was a vast change in the disease pattern.

In the first town, there were hygiene and skin issues, as well as malnourishment issues. Town two presented more lifestyle issues like diabetes, obesity, depression. Town two had more money, but the people were not better off health wise, the dynamics of the common illnesses had just changed.

We ended up breaking the record—3,000 patients seen in five days. That averages out to 600 patients being seen every day. I was seeing 100 each day, without any labs, x-rays, or ultrasounds. The students observing me were amazed that some things can be diagnosed by looking at the tongue. I told them about Pakistan, about how physical exams were often all we had when diagnosing a patient.

Another consideration to take here contrasted with the United States healthcare system: The issue of sex outside of wedlock. When I was working with patients, I had to ask about it because the possibilities for pregnancy and certain diseases increased with sexual activity. This was completely different than in Pakistan, where if you were not married, there were no children. These types of questions were uncomfortable for me, but I had to get used to asking them. So, in Guatemala, I began asking, like I had in America, "Do you have children?" The unwed women would look at me peculiarly, "No, I'm not married." Here, you could assume that if the women were not married, there was no sexual activity, thus no children. This is unlike the United States where women have children out of wedlock without much stigma.

This first medical mission caused something in me to stir. I felt that I was missing something in my life. For all these years I felt like I needed to be doing more to serve humanity and the people in need around the world, and this opportunity was giving me a taste of what was possible outside of the United States.

Sadly, the community of doctors that gives back to the world in need has suffered losses too. At times, doctors lose their lives because those being served kill their doctor when the belief differs, or they look different, or because the person doesn't practice faith like their killer does. Dr.

Dendi was killed in Pakistan, after traveling from the US to provide medical help, free of cost, to serve people in need. He was a brilliant cardiologist. He was murdered simply because he belonged to our sect of Islam. There are perils to being doctors in other countries. He went to help and was killed; it is a sad reality that we face in the field.

Another doctor was Dr. Kazani, who was practicing in Pakistan, when he was slain while getting ready to have dinner. He was a very dedicated doctor. He heard someone knock at the door, and thinking it was a patient needing assistance, he went and opened the door. When he answered the door, there was a man with a long knife in his hand who attacked him. He was stabbed because he belonged to our community. His three daughters and son are practicing doctors and serving humanity now. This was another member of our sect that was killed for his faith. Out of his three daughters and son, they are all doctors.

Another doctor, a friend of my husband's, was a very talented orthopedic surgeon. He had gone to the same med school as I had, and he was the best. We were already here in America, it was truly a lifesaver to come here. He was murdered because of success and his religious beliefs.

There never seems to be a good reason to take out the people trying to help. We see it here with first responders and violent crime. Unfortunately, the regard and respect for life, from the past, no longer exists in the same capacity.

Ideals of selfless service and dedication, that my

grandfather had demonstrated many decades ago, was in front of me in the tangible sense. I was given a chance to help this portion of humanity and provide them with the care they deserved. I decided that I should do more of this. I started going there twice a year, or whenever I was needed, to lead the medical mission, which we will talk more in depth about in the next chapter.

Chapter Fourteen

Medical Mission

When the mission is medical care, the people serving and those being served are blessed.

Life has taken turns that I hadn't originally expected or planned for, and that isn't a bad thing. My husband and I have talked often about giving back to society in ways that benefit people that cannot repay us for our help. There is something about volunteering service to those in need that adds value to life; that is priceless.

After the first medical mission, we began doing them once or twice each year. In one of those missions, there was a woman who insisted on seeing an American doctor. I was standing in my cubicle with students, and when I saw her walking towards us, I began to tell the students that she was clearly in pain, and they could assess patients before they were even examining them, if they caught them on their way in.

Analyzing patients upon sight allows the physician to be ahead of the examination process, which allows us to ask questions based on our observations. When we began to check her over, we found a huge skin lesion on her foot. It was most likely cancerous, so we referred her to a local hospital for surgery. There were various townships that we worked within while on medical missions, so I inquired about this woman. It was

161

very sad finding out that she had showed up to get the surgery, and her family had come to take her home due to financial hardships. I often wonder what ended up happening to her, but it is sad that she didn't get the help she needed.

The first trip had opened my eyes to some of the realities of third world countries. There were people walking around with high blood pressure, without blood sugar checks for years, and coping with other medical issues that seem easily managed in a first world country.

The people would take their medications for the first month, while the medicine was free, but after that, they wouldn't spend the money to continue care. This is a problem with chronic illnesses, because regular management would prevent worse symptoms and conditions. When this is not an option, amputations or other extreme measures must be taken later due to the inability to manage symptoms of chronic disease long-term.

Access to medical care wasn't like it is in the United States. We have urgent cares, walk-in clinics, hospitals, doctor's offices—they have the medical missions and medical facilities where the care is either free or the cost is nominal, but the standards are low and the facilities are not kept up on or hygienic. Regular medical access to professionals is not available. There are people suffering who need immediate care. They go without or die. It is sad to see.

Then there were the problems with education and orientation to health. In the United States, people know that diabetes can be very serious—there, they have no clue about the consequences of not managing diabetes. Due to lack of knowledge, they would rather buy junk food than spend money on medical supplies and necessary medications. Sadly, their diets and lack of health information has led to serious issues like malnourishment, skin diseases, and a plethora of hygiene issues. We did what we could to educate them about the value of fresh fruits and vegetables in their diets.

The education level in the United States impresses me. I respect my patients and their diligence in following up on my recommendations. They are great at bringing their blood sugar down and improving their blood pressure readings. Many Americans get their labs done religiously, which makes my job easier, when bloodwork is up to date. Waiting for results can prolong my ability to diagnose an illness, and time is of the essence when dealing with disease, so it is very helpful when patients do what we ask them to do in a timely manner.

Another huge issue, that we can take for granted, is access to clean water. In Guatemala, and many third world countries, water is contaminated or not readily available. There are gutter systems that contaminate the water supply regularly. In some countries, even the children will travel long distances on foot to make long treks back to their homes, just for water. It isn't a faucet away.

While we were there, we couldn't drink the water. We were only drinking bottled water. I still got sick, for a whole month the first time! There were students that ended up sick as well. Maybe from eating undercooked food or from the dishes being washed in the water, I'm not sure. It is safe to say that if we were getting sick, the people living there were not made better by their regular circumstances.

Health issues were caused by many different things. The houses had wood burning stoves inside of them, and these were small houses. This caused asthma, breathing issues, carbon monoxide poisonings, and the like. The quality of air was further compromised by ashes from volcanic activity. It is hard to believe that such a beautiful lush green land could hold such contamination.

My husband has traveled there with me almost every time. We went on a medical mission to Africa, as well. This medical mission was far different.

In Africa, we weren't seeing patients, we were training and lecturing the doctors. I went with the doctors from John Hopkins and Canadian doctors with the sole goal of education.

Our first stop was Ghana. We were teaching the doctors to do laparoscopic surgery, so they wouldn't have to open the belly. I gave a lecture on pre-op evaluations and labs. We talked with the medical students in Ghana to encourage them in their studies and pursuit of making the medical field more advanced. It was exciting to see their energy and hunger for knowledge. The teachers were using pigs to teach this surgery.

Next up, we flew from Ghana to Liberia. The next day we were supposed to go to Liberia's Hospital to teach them to do hernia repair with mesh. There was a high rate of incidences of hernias in Tapeta. They had instances where the hernia reached the knee.

Honestly, I thought this road trip was the final

one of my life. We were headed to a remote area in the mountains, and we were supposed to get there by UNICEF helicopters. There was an incredible lack of communication that had made it seem like the helicopters weren't coming, so we got into three SUVs sent by the hospital.

My husband and I sat in the backseat of the SUV, praying, while the driver navigated the treacherous terrain. We left at ten a.m. and were expected to arrive at our destination in two to three hours, but we didn't arrive until nine that night. The dangerous trip was made worse by the unpaved roads in the mountains. There was so much dust that the wipers were on continuously, yet we still couldn't see through the windshield. We were so scared! I can laugh about it now, but it certainly wasn't funny at the time.

When we arrived in Liberia, the hospital was great. They had top-of-the-line machines. China built the hospital and all the equipment had Chinese writing. The problem was that no one knew how to use the machines due to the language differences. We made educational rounds in the hospital. Lectures were presented to the local doctors. The surgeons with our group assisted and taught during live surgeries on humans.

TRANSITIONING ROLES

We continued to go to Guatemala. Every time, we saw many patients and we felt that whatever we were doing was not enough. We were giving them medicine for a month, but it runs out, so the patient must go without until they can receive care again.

The fact that there were so few trauma centers, and that the existing facilities were so far apart, really moved on me. Trauma centers are far apart, and the level of care given by public hospitals is suboptimal. We heard ambulances on the road, working to help save lives in crisis. Because of the need assessed by the medical missions, our worldwide leader in London decided it was important to build a hospital, which took tons of planning and fundraising—to the tune of $3 million. That is a huge undertaking, from start to finish.

The organization assessed that there was a need for a hospital in the area to provide quality care at low costs for the people. The organization got the concept of the hospital and it was approved by the World-Wide Leader. The funds were raised by generous doctors and donors. Our faith tells us that when we spend one dollar, the money is multiplied. Then there are more blessings to multiply the money given, and the giver. The hospital was founded in June of 2017.

The hospital was completed in October of 2018. When the hospital was finished, I was given the responsibility of Director of Internal Medicine Department. I was happy to commit to that.

When the hospital was inaugurated, the Worldwide Leader of our faith came down for the opening ceremonies. He was involved in the inauguration of the hospital, which was amazing for my husband and myself—to see the success of something we had wished for being blessed by the highest spiritual person in our faith.

The Worldwide Leader had thirty to forty people with him, but when it was time to visit the medical ward, I was the doctor assigned with the local Guatemalan internist, to that area, on that floor, at the time.

After I had shown him the department and the rooms on the ward, he asked, "Is there any doctor retiring soon?"

I hadn't anticipated that question. I thought he would ask about the number of nurses and doctors. I had no plans to retire at the time, but out of my mouth popped, "Yes, I am retiring." I didn't even know I was going to say that, but the result was I was dedicating my services to this hospital.

When the day was over, I was sitting with Qamar, and I relayed the events to him, inquiring about his thoughts and feelings regarding the quick impromptu conversation. "What should I do now?"

Qamar was completely supportive. We agreed that we could cut down on the practice at home to work solely as volunteers. That would be dedicating our work to God alone and make life much simpler. To work without money seems scary, yet that was why my husband had been diligent all these years with our money. Now that there was a need and an opportunity, we could answer the call.

The hospital is built now, and the new focus is the running of the hospital. A beautiful clean hospital, running at American standards, in a third world country. I was honored with the task of being the Executive Medical Director of the entire hospital. The American doctors that come to the medical mission are there to mentor and train the local doctors.

Donations built this hospital, and for now, the hospital is being provided for by donations as well. We offer a lot of free services for people who cannot afford treatment. This presents challenges, but the people involved are all in, so the money continues to keep the hospital running. Fortunately, our community is full of dedicated people who understand that when you spend for God's purposes, He blesses the giver abundantly. The real secret of earning pure money, money that gains blessings, is to give and be blessed like the money can never end, much like the 300 rupees I had in college.

Humanity First organizes a Medical Mission every so often. I had been involved before, but this time, as Medical Director of the hospital. There is so much need, and we work to use the funds correctly to help as many people as we can. The goal is always for a high standard of care while seeing as many people as we can. Our efforts touch a lot of lives, and that is intentional.

I was tasked with organizing the medical aspects of the camp after the hospital was inaugurated. We would start at eight in the morning, every day, and be available long after the sun had gone down. The Guatemalan people were exceedingly grateful. The need is great there. The camp's goal is to help very poor people get the medical care that they need. We were in the town where the hospital is, and we were able to use all the resources (labs, testing instruments, x-rays, etc.) at our disposal. It was a great learning experience for the students of the University of Michigan.

I will now be in Guatemala more than I am in

the United States, as the Medical Director of the whole hospital. The bittersweet part of my transitioning role is that there are numerous patients in the US that I care about and love. I don't want to stop taking care of them. The responsibility in Guatemala is tremendous and my efforts are necessary to make this hospital a success, since I have been entrusted with the role of Medical Director of the hospital. As I finish this book, I reread it on the plane rides, making sure every word is in its place. This has made life a journey, and one that I am thoroughly enjoying.

I feel that even though I was serving humanity in America, I was still making decent money, which somehow doesn't make it service in my mind. Working just to serve, without any money, is a different feeling that I am not sure there are words for. It is felt in the heart. It's time for that.

I want to use the rest of my productive life to serve the poor and needy, without getting anything in return monetarily. My return is blessings and the mercy of my Lord, my God. There is so much beauty in being able to selflessly give to those in need. This has become my life.

Chapter Fifteen

Personal Reflections on Healthcare

Opinions should only be based on experience.

I feel very blessed to be a medical professional. As a provider, I can alleviate some suffering of the human race and provide support to help heal sore bodies and minds. As an internist, I have enjoyed sharing the personal joys and hardships of my various patients and have supported them in the times of their difficulties. This may be the unsung work of medical professionals, and it may also be the part that saves the most lives.

Can you imagine seeing a doctor at the hardest time of your life, and you feel that they don't care about the outcome—whether you survive or die? I have had patients that believed that about their former doctors, and I would think, How sad?! How do you fight for your life, or deal with an illness, when you don't think your doctor is on your side?

When I get the honor to fulfill my duty to God by working with a patient, I make sure that I am praying for them and listening to them. There is nothing better than going to bed every night and resting in the fact that I have done all I can do, which creates the only option of leaving the rest to God. I will uncover every stone, through medical tests, that I can. Once I have done my part, I know that the Creator is doing His part.

Diagnosing disease on time can save lives, but

preventing disease is even better than diagnosing disease early. To do that, a primary care physician should be helping with diet and encouraging lifestyle changes. If I had a dollar for every patient that I counseled, to watch what they ate and get the right exercise, who ignored the advice and later ended up with Diabetes II, I would be retired already. And for every patient that could follow those guidelines to escape Diabetes II but are too stuck in their patterns of eating and not exercising, it makes my heart break.

Doctors don't save people from themselves, only the patient can do that. We just manage the diseases caused by poor lifestyle choices, to the best of our ability. We fall ill because of our own mistakes, and God in His mercy heals us, according to the Holy Quran. Most chronic debilitating adult illnesses, like Diabetes II, heart disease, hypertension, obesity, osteo-arthritis and some others, are because of bad lifestyle choices.

Since the very beginning, medical providers have been given respect and are expected to provide the best professional behaviors. If a doctor does something outside of the understood norms, between a patient and a doctor, it makes headlines. It almost must, because this is still a sacred relationship in society. We are trusted in life and death situations, and with everything in between. Doctors that make wrong diagnoses for financial gain have been making headlines. This breach of trust puts the standard doctor-patient relationship in jeopardy.

There has been a unique relationship of trust between the patients and their doctors. When a patient comes to a doctor, he/she expects that the doctor has full knowledge and expertise in the field and will be providing the best opinion regarding their condition. Therefore, doctors continue to read the current research. It is why we go to conferences and listen to other doctors at seminars. There is no such thing as going to school once and expecting the learning in our field is complete. We are constantly expected to be on top of cutting-edge research. We are expected to know what new treatment options are available in our field. The continuity of medical education is the recertification which requires doctors to pass the boards every ten years (for me).

By practicing medicine in the USA, with the experience of having started my medical career in Pakistan, I have experienced two wide variations in the approach and resources associated with healthcare, plus the use and misuse of these resources. There is a lot to say here, so buckle in.

Thinking back on my journey, where I started and where I am now, I feel accomplished. I am content with my decision to adopt this profession as a provider. God gave me the opportunity to serve humanity, and God granted me respect and success in this field.

As a physician, I have the unique ability to serve my patients, support them and their families, and make a difference in many people's days, if not their lives. It is very humbling to touch so many parts of a patient's life, and that is why I cover my patients with prayer. They were brought to me by the Creator, and it is my duty to help them, and He will give me the correct knowledge and foresight to run the right tests and know what I am seeing in the results.

As a doctor running my own office, I can describe my usual day, from room to room. One room will be full of laughter, and in the next room, I could be wiping tears from the eyes of a patient who lost a loved one or found out that they could lose their life. I could be giving good news in one room and then go straight to sharing bad news in the next room. The roller coaster of emotions keeps me running in circles, a gamut of heights and depths.

It can be exhausting. It takes a toll on a physician's life to be the bearer of bad news and good news alike. Our bodies release chemicals like adrenaline, dopamine, cortisol, endorphins, the list could go on and on. Imagine all these chemicals dumping into the body and brain, stimulating chemical responses, every fifteen minutes or less, as doctors rush from room to room to see as many patients as possible.

The system in the United States seems to punish the poor for being poor. The middle class seems to get it even worse—at the top, medical care is affordable. At the bottom, government assistance takes over and makes sure that care is given. The middle class makes too much for help, but they are too poor to afford medical care out-of-pocket. There are less options for medications and treatments, depending on which insurances or self-pays are involved. It is never a good feeling to see that my hands are tied when I am working to help a patient.

As a female physician, one must deal with the aspects of getting married, the raising and upbringing of any children we may have and focusing on their nutritional needs and emotional stability. Being a doctor doesn't excuse us from the responsibility of taking care of our household while simultaneously answering calls to take care of our patients. Your family is ultimately your responsibility, which means when you leave work—whether that is the hospital, your clinic, or the office (doing mounds of paperwork)—there is still more to do.

In addition to these never-ending responsibilities, you have more responsibilities, amongst your friends and other relatives. There are expectations and demands from others, that if given double the hours in each day (with no sleep), will keep us on our feet running. That means, we must prioritize and accept that some things must wait for another day.

Clearly, doctors don't get to live on sparsely populated islands with 'Do Not Disturb!' signs when they are off duty, although that would be nice at times. I am not saying that male physicians don't have their own surplus of responsibilities, I am just choosing to speak about the female aspects that I am familiar with.

It seems easy to forget that doctors are humans—it seems like the patients forget and so the doctors forget. We go through the same medical, social, physical, mental, spiritual, and psychological challenges, just like everyone else. We aren't exempt from human toils, just because we went to med school or because we are in a different tax bracket, as people tend to believe. We disagree with our spouses and things happen to our children that we can't control, like everyone else! Doing kindness to mankind doesn't exempt us from heartache. I wish that were true, but then everyone would be a doctor!

For some reason, when a doctor is sick, people

look at it differently. The doctors feel embarrassed and won't share their own medical issues with anyone. It is almost looked on, from the outside, like, "You are supposed to heal others, but you can't heal yourself." Never mind that a podiatrist can't do what a cardiologist can, and vice versa. There is some unwritten universal rule that leaves sick doctors in the closet, because we don't want to be perceived as unable to perform our job and duties. The fear is tangible, and it is that we will have to stop practicing medicine if, heaven forbid, we ended up ill.

There was a cardiologist who was having trouble standing, and people didn't want to go to him anymore because he couldn't stand on his own. He was overweight which was causing health issues. Obviously, it is difficult to trust a person who is contradictory to their own practice. Would you see a dentist with rotten teeth? The cardiologist had neglected his health, and the wear and tear on his health acted as a deterrent to patients. That is one reason doctors must focus on their personal health. It is easy to neglect exercise with the long hours doctors put in, but it is vital for a doctor's health that they follow the same recommendations that they would give a patient pertaining to healthy lifestyle choices.

No matter how stressed you are in your personal life, you must enter a room with a big smile and a giant loud greeting. Maybe we aren't ill, maybe we are just having a tough day—it doesn't matter. We are always expected to be jolly and happy. There is no sullen doctor expectation, so when we come in, "HI! Mrs. So-and-So, how are you!?" Then we react appropriately to the information we are given by the patient. This brings life and energy to the patient who is worried about their own health problems. The patient gets to see a happy doctor walking in, who has no other care in the world than them—right in that moment.

I remember the day when I had just gotten to work, in the morning, and was starting up my computer to start seeing patients as soon as the door opened. This day wasn't going to be a 'normal' day at the office.

My sister, who was the sole caregiver to my mother, three hours away by air, called through FaceTime. She was showing me our mother, and I immediately saw there was an acute change in her condition. She was in respiratory distress. I could tell it was her last few moments. The worst part was I could not say this in front of my mom, I didn't want to make her panic.

I asked my sister to step out of the room and advised her to call our other sisters on FaceTime. We were saying goodbye to our mother, all five sisters over video chat, seeing our beloved mother taking her last breaths.

I had no control over my emotions. I was agitated, walking in and out of my office, telling my office staff that my mom was leaving me. There were patients in the lobby, all waiting, getting restless. Then they started arguing with the receptionist, as they did not want to see the physician's assistant, like I needed them to. They had been waiting for weeks to see me, and they were not taking no for an answer.

I stepped out in the lobby and informed all the patients that my mom had just left this world, but I would still see them. I managed to see as many patients as I could, with my heart not accepting the fact of my loss! My mother had passed away, and instead of being able to grieve properly, I had to entertain clients. I would go alone in my office, cry, and then go to the next exam room to see the waiting patient with a smile! Looking back, I am glad that I was able to be there for my patients that day, but I also wish that I had been granted the ability to grieve instead of displacing my sorrow.

Multiple factors play a role in practicing medicine. It's important to realize that when one decides to adopt the medical profession, they must agree to put patients first. That means that personal needs and family needs come second. This is a huge adjustment. A doctor's responsibility is to their patients—to take care of them and make sure we are available in their times of need. This can prove difficult when children are young and a patient needs you—you find out very quickly that in order to keep the trust of patients, you better pack up and make it to their side in their time of need. This means that, at times, doctors will miss important life events.

It's not like dealing with machines—if it's not working, leave it for tomorrow. We deal with humans, and we can't say "My time is over, sorry, even if you are critical, I will go home now and see you tomorrow, if you are still alive!" Humans have feelings and their lives are valuable, so we must do everything within our power, as doctors, to save them.

The other unknown secret is that the doctor is a consultant. We are not here to enforce treatment. The risk is that the patient may not tell the doctor that they are not taking their medications, and the doctor increases the dosage thinking that the medication needs adjusted. Sometimes we get messages from pharmacies saying that the patient hasn't filled prescriptions for a long time, so they most likely aren't taking the prescription. Then we follow up but if they are not non-compliant, there isn't much we can do.

Our role in healthcare is not to babysit, but to consult and advise our patients. I can give medications that can help, but it is up to the client to take the medicine on the correct schedule. If they take them all at once, we may be looking at an overdose situation. If the patient doesn't take the medicine as prescribed, then the medication may not do what it was intended to do. Our intentions are to help and use our expertise to inform and educate the patient with all the intricate details of treating, or not treating, the medical problem

Sometimes, the doctor treats the patient with a command to follow the directions, and then the doctor makes it a cause of personal insult, or an ego issue, if the patient refuses to follow advice. Documentation is important so we are not implicated in lawsuits. We need to focus; our job as providers is not to enforce decisions upon the patient, it's the patient's autonomy and decision to follow (or not to follow) the directions of the doctor.

This also means that whatever might happen to the patient for refusing medical advice and treatment is not the doctor's fault or problem. Sometimes, the doctor gets offended or lives in fear of lawsuits because a patient did not follow the recommendations. We must get over that. There will be plenty of patients that will not do what they are advised to do. It's part and parcel with our career choice.

Medicare has started a process called Meaningful Use of resources, with the expectations of preventative care, where there are expectations of mammograms, colonoscopies, and other regular tests need to be done. But the numbers are skewed by patients not getting tests done. We order them, sometimes the patients do not show up for the tests. In medicine now, everyone will be paid differently based on performance status. If someone orders more tests, and spends more money, they will get paid less. Likewise, if a doctor orders less tests, spending less, then they will get paid more.

The practice of medicine, nowadays, is not as simple as way-back-when. In older days, a doctor would set off from the dinner table to go to patient's homes, with a small bag and maybe, the doctor would end up writing a few prescriptions after an examination, but most likely the patients had the remedy in their medicine cabinet already.

There was not a pill for every side effect and illness. Now there is a pill for everything…Do you have acne? There's a pill. Are you nauseous? Pill. Do you have flatulence? I have a pill for you. There are many reasons certain treatments are better than others, but there are common daily annoyances that can be fixed with diet and lifestyle changes. There is a pill and then there is another pill to take care of the side effects. There is pill used to build bones, but when you take that, the side effect can be ulcers—so we treat the ulcers with a pill that can cause brittle bones that break. It's dizzying to keep up with. If we get better at preventative care through lifestyle choices, we will create less issues through medication.

Informed consent is a huge deal in medicine. The patient has the right to understand everything—the risks and rewards to a treatment plan, all options available, what the side effects of medications might be, before they even agree to a treatment plan. It is the doctor's responsibility to provide this information, many doctors are not doing a good job when it comes to true informed consent. A patient does not have the knowledge that a doctor is trained for in medical school, and thus should not be expected to understand all the aspects of their treatment plan.

The problem with true informed consent seems to be the time constraints. With any given treatment plan, there are a great deal of things to go over. Many doctors have a nurse hand the patient a piece of paper to sign, that says, "I understand what is being presented to me," without being given the full picture. Surgeons must provide their expectations of how they are conducting the surgery and what could happen—what can go wrong or right. Then they leave a paper, and get it signed.

In the case of the DNR (do not resuscitate), many surgeons want to waive the DNR, by removing it so they can resuscitate. They want to resuscitate, because they don't like to have a table death on their record. They sometimes put patients on breathing machines to save their name, instead of honoring their wishes to not have that life saving measure.

End of life wishes must be honored to preserve the medical field. Certain apparatuses in certain situations do not add anything to the quality of life, only to the quantity. The statistics are affected by mere hours and days, so to the people waiving the DNR, it is worth it to ignore the piece of paper that was thought out and expected to be upheld. It almost seems like our once honored field has become robotic. The protocols— instead of dealing with humans, we are expected to deal with adjusting medications by looking at paper. It is quite sad when I sit and consider it all.

At times, it feels like we, doctors, are not the decision makers of the possible treatment options. Insurance companies are, by having a list of possible things we can do that they will pay for. And pharmaceutical companies are, by running ads for you to "ask your doctor if this treatment is right for you." Pharmaceutical companies discontinue medications, deliver new medications, and change prices on medications, until doctors must follow the ebb and flow of the companies instead of what might be best for the patient. The offset is the store brands are much cheaper, when available, and work about the same.

It's great that we do research and try to investigate new options for disease treatment. It's not bad to keep on having more and more options available for the patient to choose from. The problem lies in the reality that most of the time, we are not able to prescribe the drug of choice. If I know something works for a certain client, there are other factors that go into them receiving the medication. Sometimes insurance companies want us to use a medicine that may have more side effects, is stronger than the patient might need, or less appropriate for the specific condition. This is merely due to the fact the drug company has given them a special discount on that medication. In my professional opinion, health shouldn't be relegated to price points that shift based on the stock of a pharmaceutical company.

Another issue we deal with is the concept of prior authorization becoming more and more of a hindrance in a patient's diagnosis and treatment. Insurance companies control their expenses by not letting a specific test be done or by not letting a patient get the appropriate medication. Sometimes the doctor must spend hours trying to get one medication or test done for a patient. For some doctors, where every minute is counted in terms of dollars, they don't want to spend that time. We pay office staff to obtain authorizations for these things. Most of the time, they don't authorize anyways, so these resources are used to act on behalf of the patient but are not beneficial. Some doctors might let the patient be left alone or just order the high risk or preferred drug to bypass jumping through hoops.

Medicare does not cover a patient's expense of treatment in a nursing home if the hospital stay was not more than three nights. It doesn't matter what the patient may need in the long-term, there are rules governing how things get paid. Again, the well-being of human beings is selfishly sacrificed at the expense of paper and coin...I find it a little more than sickening.

The kicker, or the joke, is that it would cost less than three months of expenses in a nursing facility per minimal day cost in the hospital. Obviously, there are different levels in care facilities, but if you are looking at a $3,333 per month care facility versus a minimum $10,000 per day stay in the hospital, then it would make more sense financially to allow the patient NINE MONTHS of prolonged and constant care, which would amount to the same three days in the hospital. So, is it really about the money?

In my opinion, it seems like our country punishes the poor for being poor. They allow higher interest rates, higher insurance rates, and for banks to punish negative accounts, when clearly the people with these issues don't have money to begin with. The care facilities available to the poor are not as nice as the ones available to the rich, and the sick and dying must go through fire-laced paperwork hoops to get the care that they deserve as human beings made in the image of God. Money is not made in the image of God, but it is esteemed higher than God in places.

Many patients cannot afford the expenses, out-of-pocket, so they are forced to take the risk of going home and jeopardizing their life with an unsafe environment. At times, patients are brought to the nursing homes at the end of their life, but they must undergo physical therapy for their expenses to be covered by Medicare. Families will sometimes resist pain medication, to keep their family member alert, but we take comfort very seriously. Other families will go out of their way to make their family member comfortable. That's for the elderly patients that have family that still visit regularly. More often, elderly patients have nothing and no one to speak for them.

As I started my medical journey in the USA, I was told, "Documentation, documentation documentation!"

Instead of being able to care for patients, I had to focus on covering my backside. I became proficient at the paperwork, especially when using a voice to text system, but I still wish the industry was more care oriented.

My senior resident taught me that if I did an exam and did not document it, then to the powers that be, it means that I didn't do the exam. On the other hand, if I did not do an exam, but documented that I completed the exam, well, that means I did it. Which is crazy to me. If I did but didn't write it, I didn't. If I didn't, but I wrote it, I did. Backwards and morally wrong, the practice of defensive medicine was very new to me. We spent hours writing our notes, and we only spent five minutes with the patient!

Another byproduct of defensive medicine is doing extra unnecessary tests so that we don't miss anything. This sounds good in theory, but it manifests higher costs of care, which causes problems for the insurance companies who get stricter with us. It's a very ugly and vicious cycle.

Overtreating is another evil of modern medicine. If the patient doesn't have a source of infection, you treat with antibiotics anyway to be proactive, so that nothing is missed. Consequently, now we are dealing with multiple drug resistant organisms, meaning those antibiotics will no longer kill the bacteria. We are starting antibiotics stewardship programs after decades of using antibiotics inappropriately, just because we are afraid of lawsuits. In other countries there is too much access to medication; here it seems more controlled, with more regulations, yet the opioid epidemic rages, and we must admit that a large percentage of overdoses and addictions are to prescription medications. It's crazy.

There was a patient that took their daughter to the hospital, and the emergency room doctor gave them amoxicillin (an antibiotic) for the flu. The wife called me a week later, after it was realized that she had mono and the little girl had an adverse reaction to the antibiotic, and said, "Why would they have given her antibiotics? The flu is a virus."

She had warned her husband, and his response was, "Honey, you're not a doctor. We will follow the rules." I didn't have an answer for her, but I understood her frustration.

Ultimately, don't go against what your doctor says unless you have gotten other professional opinions, but insist on informed consent. That is more than the little handouts that we give. Informed consent truly goes over risks and rewards, fully. You should know the consequences of different treatment options, and you should hear about options—not just one thing and that is what you're doing. You have a right to make decisions on your treatment plan. Afterall, you are the one going through the treatment and dealing with the ramifications of certain medications.

In underdeveloped countries, the doctor has the final say. Patients are helpless and without many resources. They appreciate the doctor's little attention, because they may only go to get care under dire circumstances. Here, the availability of care is so vast that people go to the doctor for colds, the flu, and everything in between. Can't sleep all night? Call your doctor. Having heartburn after eating pizza all week? Call the doctor.

I am not putting patients down, but there are certain common-sense things I wish patients would listen to me about. For instance, putting the phone down or turning the television off an hour before bed will help you sleep. The mind must calm down from stimuli, and if you don't give your brain the opportunity to unwind, it will be more difficult to sleep. Instead, the common practice is to give a sleeping pill that can make it near impossible to ever sleep naturally again.

In underdeveloped countries, it is normal for less than half of the population to have access to a doctor who can perform a thorough history and physical examination and then provide appropriate treatment. Many patients that are unable to afford the medical treatment that is available to them end up going to quacks and use alternative medicine.

All over the world, there are people dying without any medical treatment or even an established diagnosis. How crazy this must sound to American readers. We are spoiled here, and we don't even appreciate it! Although, what I am calling alternative medicine in third world countries is also different than what it is here, but that is entirely another subject.

The polypharmacy is another outcome of overmedicating and trusting in pills for everything, rather than making lifestyle changes. Polypharmacy is where multiple medications are being used to treat a patient for one illness. When patients are started on medications by their primary providers, then by consultants, there are times that unnecessary medications are not stopped.

This happens more often with the elderly who end up on multiple blood pressure medications, blood thinners, and stomach medications, to name a few. There are side effects to these medications that leads to the start of more medications to manage the side effects. The most common cause of altered mental states in elderly patients can be attributed to medications, or what is called drug-to-drug interactions. Instead of all the medications being investigated, a doctor may think that an antipsychotic will help with the new aggressive behaviors, when the full picture might point to a clash of medications causing the mental state of the patient. It is important to follow-up with primary physicians and ask for reviews of medications.

In other countries, the pharmacy doesn't need to be run by a pharmacist. The drugstore person has more power in third world countries and may suggest treatment to a patient, through the ability to give medications without a written prescription from the doctor.

All high-risk medications and drugs that are controlled in the United States are available over-the-counter other places. Anyone can get them, yet we don't see the problem of drug addiction quite like the United States experiences, which might be a difference in the reporting standards. The narcotics epidemic we are dealing with in the US is staggering and shocking to me. I understand that there are doctors that will overprescribe narcotics, but my mind also reels at the number of people that take serious medications to get high. Where did they learn these behaviors?

Is it that we have conditioned them to believe two

things? First, society has conditioned people to believe that doctors are always acting in the best interest of their patients. We are led to blindly trust people in the medical profession, even though there is proof that some doctors take death into their own hands. More recently doctors have admitted to fabricating certain illnesses to make more money— (Hint—the illness being fabricated was cancer and the treatment being profited from was chemotherapy—which is very dangerous and damaging even to cancer patients). As a practicing medical doctor, I am left aghast at such things! I would never look to profit off a false diagnosis...the thought had never crossed my mind! It depends on the intentions of the doctor. If someone chose this profession for money, they might do these things. If they chose being a doctor to save lives, they would never do these things.

The second thing people have been conditioned to believe is: Medications fix people. Pharmaceutical companies spend a lot of money advertising. Their commercials show someone sad, and then that same actor gives a testimonial of how a medication helped them, before running off into the sunset. It gives the consumer a warm fluffy feeling, even as the commercials list more side effects than the medication fixed. Ultimately, the message was set in stone—"I had this problem, like you do, and this medicine fixed me."

So, let's travel through the entire thought process: "Doctors have our best interest in mind, and medications fix people. Therefore, if my doctor gives me a medication, I am going to get better. I don't need to ask one question or do any research. I can trust this exchange." The flip side is that there are patients who don't take essential medications vital to their wellbeing because of the long list of side effects that the pharmaceutical companies print to cover their bases.

Unfortunately, this exchange leaves very high-risk medications in the hands of patients without the education regarding the risks associated with it. In third world countries, people do have access to medications without doctors being involved, which is incredibly dangerous, in my opinion. Pharmacists are supposed to educate the patient on the medications—the dosage, whether the medication should be taken with food, whether certain foods damage the responsiveness of the medication, risks of the medication, etc.

The role of the pharmacist needs to be held to the proper standard; it is more than a handout stapled to the prescription bag. People are getting damaged by medications, due to this negligence. There are patients that aren't reassured that their medical provider will properly monitor them for side effects. The people handing patients medications are often not pharmacists, they are just techs. This practice is not safe. I want to make sure to be clear that medicine has become mechanical—expected.

Doctors try to have the patient in and out in fifteen minutes. They are forced to hurry and cannot give full disclosures which means they have to make fast decisions. Pharmacists should (and some do) help by educating the patients at the checkout. Pharmacists are known to catch when a cardiologist may have prescribed a drug that counteracts a medication from a primary care physician that the patient might have forgotten to mention. The importance of these cross-checking systems is invaluable, as at the end of the day everyone in the medical field is human.

On the other hand, when I came here, some of the medications that we were using in Pakistan were not approved by the FDA, which means other countries' patients are being put at risk. Medication safety studies ensure less damage is done to humans in the long run, and that is missing in countries without agencies, like the FDA, due to the medications not being studied correctly through animal and human studies, which leaves the medications that are available unregulated.

I have seen many ladies being hooked on anxiolytics, like benzodiazepines, by getting them from the pharmacy without being monitored in underdeveloped countries. I have also seen it in the United States, because of the liberal application of medication. There are even some people who are taking strong antipsychotic medications without any monitoring. Most medical providers follow regulations about monitoring these drugs, but if the patient doesn't follow-up with their doctor, the outcome could be dangerous. This is detrimental to the long-term outcome of patients. It may seem like a quick fix, but it can cause problems for years to come.

In less developed countries, a doctor is the god of medicine, and no one double guesses the opinion of a doctor. If things don't go right, the outcome is considered the will of God. No lawsuits or questions come as a result! It has been my personal observation, in Pakistan and some other countries, doctors are treated like gods.

These same doctors will step into that role and behave accordingly. There was a doctor that won't turn his pages; he has a clerk who turns the pages for his signature.

I think the way that medical practices are most successful lies in the middle. It needs to be balanced. If there wasn't so much polarization of the medical field—incredibly expensive all the way to dirt cheap care; liberal application of medicine versus medicine only when it is vitally necessary; testing for everything or testing for nothing; documenting nothing while doing everything to documenting everything yet doing nothing; when people die always saying it is the will of God versus always suing the doctor in a death situation; all of these things (and this is a short list) present problems!

Let's take a shot at what balanced healthcare could look like:

I. Affordable care, in the case where someone is not wealthy enough for care, they will still receive the same care as someone who can easily afford the care. Sometimes, the costs of tests are astronomical (and treatment isn't cheap). If we could get the costs low enough, a doctor could provide care without losing a lot of money. In a tax system like the US, there could be tax breaks for services done for the poor, but not compensated. Truthfully, this is slightly how it is, but there could be better ways of going about this.

II. Medications should be available for comfort in cases where the person is at the end of their life. There is a however here: Medications should not be pushed for things they do not help with or when it isn't medically necessary. Deciding what is medically necessary should be left to the doctor, but not every patient needs pain medications. Not every patient needs anxiety meds or antidepressants. New medications should not be prescribed at every visit. A lot of times, lifestyle changes would prove more helpful. Counseling and therapy can be better than or equal to antidepressants, but that would require actual emotional work from the patient. Care should include real-life and lasting solutions as well— like therapy, counseling, behavioral modification, rehab, etc.

III. Testing should be consistent with the patient's complaints and concerns and within the doctor's range of knowledge. Insurance companies will sometimes not approve tests, which can be frustrating when a doctor thinks something may be wrong with their patient. The insurance companies should not be able to do this.

IV. Obviously, documentation is for accountability purposes, and that will always be important in the medical field. I categorically disagree with documenting false measures. I am fine with documenting what I do. The balance here is honesty, which is hard to monitor in a broken system.

V. Sometimes, it is God's will for people to die. We will all pass from this life someday. Here's the kicker— there are medical mistakes that end life, that God will allow, but it is hard to say for the patients who were willfully murdered by certain medical practices, that they were meant to die at that moment. Even if we agree that God had willed them to die at that time or they wouldn't have, the people who wrongfully killed them should be held accountable.

VI. On the flip side, we don't need to be so sue crazy that a doctor is afraid to operate in compassion due to money-crazed family members. A doctor can save thousands of patients, but one mistake could spread all over the media. There are patients who wish to stop prolonging their lives, and wish to stop any resuscitation, but their families insist on keeping them 'alive.' It is sad to watch, but we do as we are told out of fear. The medical rule is that if a patient is in their right mind and capable to make decisions, we always listen to the patient. If there is a power of attorney that goes against what the patient wants, we will hold family meetings and ethics meetings to fix the conflict. My compassion would help them be comfortable, but I would honor their wishes. There are patients that want their dignity intact, and I have watched their family members selfishly stomp on all their wishes.

For as many sad things as I see, the human condition still amazes me. I have seen families pull together and do amazing things to help their loved ones. I have seen communities pull together through tragedies. I have seen groups reach out to help someone very unlike them who was in crisis.

Between the doors of death and life, there is a large range of possibilities that affect everything I do, and it affects everything you do. If you are breathing and reading this, then you can still do the things that count. You are still capable of making decisions that can and will change the course of your life. Don't wait! As a doctor, I am urging you to get the most out of life. No one sits on their death bed wishing they had done less.

And if you are closer to death's door reading

this, it's okay! Mistakes you may have made don't matter anymore. Mend relationships, who cares if people make comments—death seems to be the best reckoner. Old stubborn grumps realize that they do love their family, and the family should allow them to wake up to that fact before passing on. It hurts me to see dying patients whose children are not coming to see them, or a dying mother who turns their children away because of past pain.

Between the doors of life and death, kindness and faith reign.

Made in the USA
Middletown, DE
13 December 2022

18459868R00108